WIL

COUNTRY PAPERBACKS
FROM DAVID & CHARLES

THE COUNTRYMAN COTTAGE LIFE BOOK
Edited by Fred Archer

FOLKLORE AND CUSTOMS OF RURAL ENGLAND
Margaret Baker

MEMOIRS OF A FEN TIGER
Audrey James

WILD FOX
Roger Burrows

WILD FOX
A COMPLETE STUDY
OF THE RED FOX

ROGER BURROWS

A DAVID & CHARLES COUNTRY BOOK

British Library Cataloguing in Publication Data

Burrows, Roger
  Wild Fox.
  1. England. Foxes. Social behaviour –
  Study regions: Gloucestershire. Tibberton.
  I. Title
  599'. 74'442

  ISBN 0-7153-9253-0

First published 1968 in hardback David & Charles (Publishers)
Limited. This paperback edition published 1988 by David & Charles
Publishers plc,
and printed in Great Britain
by Redwood Burn Limited, Trowbridge, Wiltshire
for David & Charles Publishers plc
Brunel House   Newton Abbot   Devon

*Cover photographs of the Red Fox courtesy of Dr Alan Beaumont,
Lowestoft.*

Contents

Acknowledgments

The author wishes to thank the farmers of Kent's Green for their willing co-operation and forbearance in allowing both him and the foxes studied to wander freely over their land. In particular, thanks to Christopher Whittal of Kent's Green Farm who was willing to tolerate foxes despite the losses he suffered and who in the cause of science refrained from shooting.

Thanks also are due to Geoffrey Kinns for permission to use his photographs for plates 2a, 2b, 6a, 6b, 8a, 9b, 10a, 10b, 11a, 12b, 13a, 13b, 14a, 14b, 15a, 16 and frontispiece, and to Jane Burton for plates 3b; 5a, 7a, 7b, 8b, 9a, 11b, 12a.

Grateful thanks also to T. Stanhope Sprigg who dealt with the difficult task of editing and to Tony Soper who suggested that the book should be written.

Last but not least to my mother who successfully deciphered the original draft and laboured patiently for many hours to produce the final manuscript; and to my wife who not only became virtually a 'fox widow' during the study but who also coped with the vagaries of my spelling and use of English.

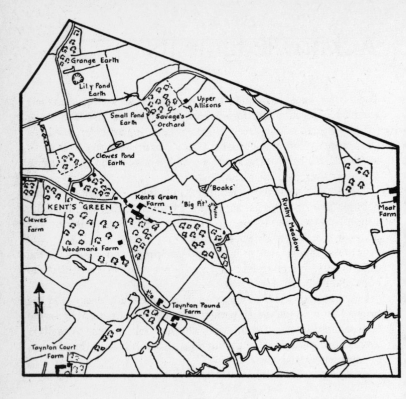

Map of area covered by fox survey, 1963–66, Kent's Green, Tibberton, Gloucestershire (Scale 3½ in = 1 mile)

Introduction

To start studying the foxes in any country area is rather like trying to solve a crime; not so much in its motivations (although a neighbour who lost some ducks certainly wanted to know who did it), but in its techniques. The first problem is just where do you start? Evidence has to be accumulated and pondered, past events must be reconstructed on the basis of the available clues, so that theories may be produced, tested and, if found unsatisfactory, abandoned. New theories must then be evolved until a satisfactory one is found; satisfactory, that is, to the investigator whose conclusions may or may not be correct. In criminal proceedings the evidence is appraised by a jury. In this book it is the reader who must judge the validity of my conclusions on the life and habits of the foxes I have studied. Many supposed facts of natural history are passed from generation to generation, often in the form of books which are collections of other people's observations and hearsay, and this is particularly true in the case of the fox. Few people stop to question printed 'facts' and still fewer make, or are in a position to make, personal observations in order to verify or refute them.

That no animal's habits were better known that those of the fox, was the conclusion I drew when I first became interested in them. In Mivart's *Monograph of the Canidae* is the comment:

> The habits of the English fox are so well known that we feel we might be dispensed from saying anything here on so trite a subject. Still, to some readers, the following words may not be altogether superfluous.

Mivart goes on to tell us that the cubs are born in April, four to six cubs to a litter, after a gestation period of sixty to sixty-four days. Cubs, he claims, become adult in one-and-a-half years or so. The inaccuracy of some of his comments on 'so trite a subject' will emerge later.

When I first tried to find the answers to questions about the everyday life of the wild fox I soon came to a full stop. I found we knew little about its food, and even less about its breeding habits; in fact, though we knew quite a lot about the silver and red fox in captivity, we knew almost nothing about the free-living animal.

My original reason for seeking information about the fox was to find out about its feeding habits. It was easy enough to discover what sort of things the fox eats in this country, but difficult to find out how much of each food item is eaten at different times of the year and whether or not the diet undergoes seasonal changes. For two years, therefore, I collected information about the food of foxes at Kent's Green and from this my interest led me on to studying the animal's general habits and way of life.

The area I studied is in West Gloucestershire, approximately six miles west of Gloucester, on the edge of the Forest of Dean. Here the mixed farmland occupies relatively (Plate 1a) low-lying land, averaging approximately 100 OD. The gently undulating land has occasional wooded hillocks rising above the general level. The bed-rock is a rather dull formation, geologically, known as Keuper Marl. An original tree cover of oak has long since disappeared but oak is still the dominant hedgerow species and also occurs in isolated clumps around small ponds and old marl pits. The latter were dug many years ago to provide a local source of lime for top-dressing the corn. Although the Keuper Marl is generally low in calcium, it must still have been thought suitable enough to dig great quantities of it rather than bring in the purer limestones from the Forest of Dean and the Cotswolds. Some of the marl pits are twenty to thirty feet deep and many now contain a permanent or temporary pond. As the marl is soft and easily eroded, the sides of the pits remain steep and poorly covered with vegetation. Many of the trees at the margins of the pits have much of their root system exposed to the air as a result of the rapid erosion of the marl from beneath them. These tangled tree roots now provide shelter for a number of animals, including the foxes who often have their earths among them. It was at one of these pits, which I named 'Big Pit' (Fig 1), that my investigations into the fox began, and I have waited for many hours in the branches and root tangles around this pit to catch a glimpse of the elusive animals either emerging from or returning to their earths. (Plate 1b).

Thanks to the willing co-operation of my farmer neighbours, par-ticularly Messrs Whittal, Clewes and Savage, I was able to study much of the area shown on the map on page 10. The section on which I concentrated most was the 100-acre Kent's Green farm and I walked regularly over this land in all seasons and at all times of the day and night. It was here that the bulk of my observations were made.

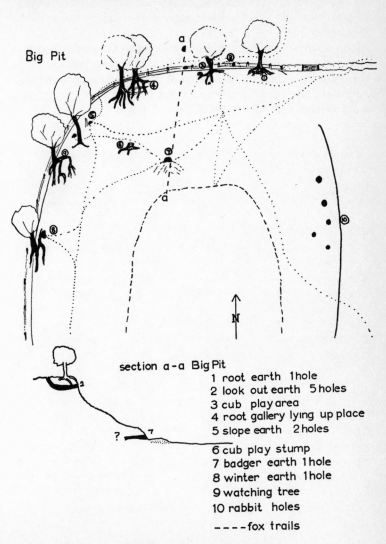

1. Big Pit, showing position of earths

All the information I obtained during my walks was entered in a fieldbook, however trivial it may have seemed at the time. When I came later to collect all the bits of information recorded, these apparently trivial single snippets, when added together, often formed a coherent whole which helped interpret the activities of the fox population.

Where it has been impossible for me to obtain the necessary information from my own observations, I have drawn on material from other sources. Wherever such material has been used, I have indicated this and given a full reference in the bibliography.

Let us now start to look for clues.

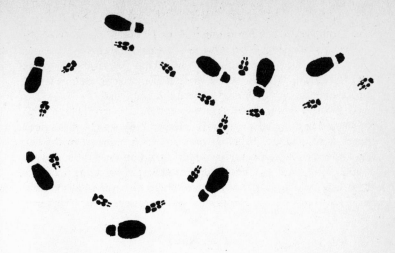

On the
Trail
of the Fox

When I began my study of the Kent's Green foxes my main concern was with feeding habits. It seemed from the available literature that very little was known about the seasonal variation in the food of the fox in Great Britain and I therefore decided to try to collect this information about the local foxes. I soon discovered that it was easier said than done.

Unless one knows a great deal about foxes, it is not easy to go out into the fields and watch them feeding; for one thing the fox usually feeds at night. But if I was unable to observe the foxes directly, how else could I tackle the problem I had set myself?

There is, of course, a solution and that is to study field sign of the fox. This involved turning myself into something of a detective—one able, that is, to find and interpret traces of the fox. Foxes leave probably more evidence of their activities in an area than most other animals, and if one can train oneself to read this sign a great deal can be discovered about the animals without ever seeing them. This

B

might sound rather unrewarding but, as I hope to show, once the 'spade work' has been done, it is possible to move from the laborious collection of clues to something to which I am now addicted—going out into the fields in the early morning or evening and watching foxes make the sign I am now so used to identifying.

What is this sign that foxes leave so conveniently around the fields for people like myself to try and interpret? By sign, I mean such things as footprints, droppings or scats, food remains, earths and temporary bedding places, bits of hair caught on vegetation, and the 'scent' of the fox. I was most interested at first in collecting fox droppings for, by analysing these, I was able to discover what the local foxes had been eating. The results will be discussed in Chapter 6.

FOOTPRINTS

These are very important signs and one needs to be familiar with the different types likely to be found. A fox's print shows four toes on both fore and hind foot, together with a prominent heel bar. Individual foxes will, of course, show slight variations but, in general, the fox footprint is narrow, the length of the print being greater than the maximum width. Claw marks are usually well defined in damp ground and are parallel with the long axis of the print, except for those of the two longest toes in the hind foot which often converge; these claw prints may even cross (Plate 2a).

Further features of a fox footprint in mud are the marks made by the hairs between the pads (Plate 2b). When moving at a normal gait, foxes place their hind feet almost in the print of the fore feet, so giving a very characteristic double print. The prints are often found in almost a straight line and look as though they were produced by a one-legged, hopping animal.

The only two other types of footprints I commonly found on my walks were those of domestic dogs and badgers. A badger's distinctive footprints—broad, five-toed, with a long heel bar and very long claw marks—form a double track which cannot be confused with those of the fox, but dog prints can, especially if there is a small terrier in the area. Fortunately, there are features which can be used to distinguish between fox and dog prints. On close examination, a dog print is found to be wider than it is long and to show four toes which diverge from one another like the fingers on a spread hand. For this reason the claw prints are not parallel, and there will be no hair marks since the sole of the dog's foot is naked. One final feature I find useful is to remember that, when trotting, a dog's body is usually held at a slight angle to the line of travel, giving it the appearance of moving slightly sideways when viewed from behind. As a result, the prints of the dog's hind feet make a completely separate trail slightly to the side of that made by the front feet. The only time I found such a double trail undoubtedly made by a fox was in late February 1965, when I suspect I was following the trail of a pregnant vixen who, because of her condition, was forced to straddle the trail.

It is said that hunters are able to distinguish the smaller footprint of the vixen from that of the dog fox, and some even claim to be able to predict the condition of the animal from a close study of its footprints in snow. A distinction I can draw is between the print made by the fore foot and that of the hind, the latter being smaller and, as already indicated, often showing convergence of the two middle toes' claws. It is also possible to distinguish between adult and cub prints, but only from April to about July while the cubs are small.

I found that the location of the footprints varied with the season but generally the most productive areas were the 'dead furrow' of a ploughed field, gateways and farm trails with bare earth, and the sides of streams and drainage ditches. Of course, the ideal tracking medium is snow, when more can be learned of a fox's movements in an hour than in many days of looking for footprints in mud and damp earth. Unfortunately, however, the amount of snow that fell in lowland Gloucestershire during the study period was so small that I had to rely on other means of tracking.

I plotted the distribution of the trails I found each month on a large-scale map of the area and was so able to discover which were the regularly used highways, knowledge which proved of great use in later stages of the study (Fig 2).

EARTHS

In my area all the earths were in the banks of the old marl pits, and most of the holes seem originally to have been dug by rabbits or, occasionally, badgers (Plate 3a). The soft marl is easily excavated and probably some of the old tunnel systems are of considerable extent.

Whilst no regularly occupied badger sets occurred at Kent's Green, I have often visited local sets which gave strong smell evidence

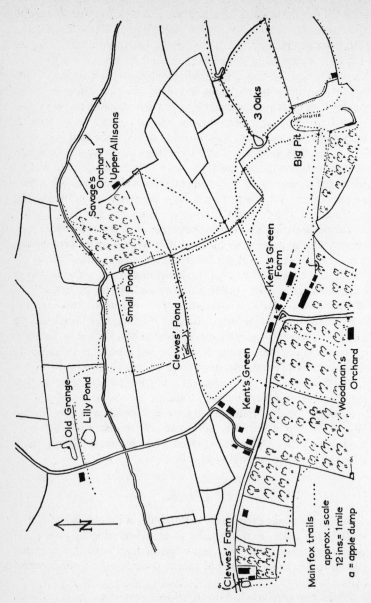

2. Sketch map of trails and the earths at Kent's Green

Old Grange

Lilly Pond

Savage's Orchard

Upper Allisons

3 Oaks

Small Pond

Clewes' Pond

Big Pit

Kent's Green Farm

Kent's Green

'Woodman's Orchard

(Clewes' Farm

N

Main fox trails ....
approx. scale
12 ins. = 1 mile
a = apple dump

of fox, particularly during the breeding season. Foxes do use badger sets during the breeding season, and probably as temporary refuges at other times.

Digging is a natural activity of the fox (Plate 3b), which uses its fore feet either singly or, rabbit-like, together. A fox's claws are very inferior weapons when compared with the badger's frontal armament but, nevertheless, they make efficient enlargers of original holes. Cubs show the digging instinct at an early age for I have watched six-week-olds making minor excavations around the entrance to the earths, either in pursuit of an elusive worm or beetle, or possibly merely for something to do.

The earths themselves may have one, two or many entrances but the majority in my area had a small number of holes. A notable exception was Clewes' Pond Earth (see Map) which had numerous holes in regular use, whereas Small Pond Earth had but one entrance. The other earths seemed to have a master hole which was used regularly and a few much smaller holes a little distance away that were often very shallow and seemed to be cub excavations which slowly got deeper as successive generations of cubs learned to dig.

Evidence of a fox family occupying any given earth is not hard to find; there will be the usual accumulation of food debris outside the earth and often in the entrances to the earths themselves or in blind tunnels. This sort of evidence remains fresh for only a few weeks as cubs do not stay very long at any one earth. The bones and feathers of prey may remain in place for many months, and it is therefore advisable to check whether the debris is fresh (a large number of adult flies is a good indication), before concluding that a family is in residence.

Fresh cub droppings outside the earths will help to establish occupancy, as will the presence of well-padded trails leading to the nearest water supply or to a play area beneath thick cover or, later, to an open 'play area', as in a field of mowing grass. These trails are usually of bruised and trampled vegetation and, with a little practice, one soon learns to determine which are in use.

The earths at Kent's Green were used almost throughout the year, except perhaps in late summer, so it was always worth while putting a few sticks over the entrances to see which were in use. I also did a little 'gardening' at the entrances by raking over some loose, fine soil in the hope of picking up footprints. But as other animals, rabbits in particular, very soon take over earths temporarily vacated by foxes there is really no simple way of knowing that a fox is in residence except by sitting and watching from a concealed spot; such watches can be most rewarding, as I shall indicate later.

BEDDING PLACES

Foxes are by no means entirely subterranean in their dwelling places, and surface beds can often be found. Their location varies from the base of a thick hedge to a simple depression in snow, other favoured places being beneath tangled tree roots, an area of long mowing grass, bramble patches and the lower forks of inclined trees. All situations have been found at Kent's Green but the most favoured was an overgrown drainage ditch with a very thick hedge on one side.

During the summer, foxes are frequently flushed from cornfields, particularly when combine harvesting operations start. Often they are cubs that lie up in this position but adults, too, seem to like the protection of ripening corn crops. In the autumn, local kale crops seem to take the place of corn so far as the fox is concerned and at this time of year there is probably a considerable potential food supply in them, particularly slugs and birds which, like the fox, find food and protection there.

If the term 'bedding place' conjures up a picture of a well-lined, warm, purpose-made structure, this is far from the truth so far as foxes' 'beds' are concerned. It seems that a fox's requirements are merely to be concealed and yet still be in the sun, especially in winter, at the same time having escape routes in various directions in case of emergency.

Snow bedding places are used during the winter as temporary resting places during the night's perambulations. These consist of a patch of flattened snow with, possibly, a dropping, the remains of a meal and perhaps a few fox hairs imbedded in the snow. As we shall see in the next chapter, surface bedding places are mainly used in the early months of the year.

FOX TRAILS

These are not so well defined as those of badgers, partly due to the lightness of the fox's step compared with the heavy plantigrade tread of the badger.

As already indicated, fox trails can often be discovered in winter following closely the 'dead furrow' of a ploughed field. In my experience, the fox seldom crosses the ploughed land but, on the few occasions I have seen them do so, it is quite striking how clear-cut are the footprints on even the heaviest, wettest, freshly-turned soil. This is, of course, in marked contrast to the shapeless depression caused by the human booted foot that seems to accumulate half the soil of the field on its sole after taking but a few steps. The clarity of the fox print is possibly because the hairs on the feet, and the extreme flexibility of the foot itself, prevent undue accumulations of mud. Even so, I think it is because the going is difficult that the fox does not usually cross freshly-ploughed land; if it does, it sinks into the soft earth and increases the physical effort of moving, just as we find it tiring to walk in soft, deep snow.

The way the fox keeps to the field margins in winter is most marked, and I do not think this is entirely due to the availability of small rodents driven from the open fields into the hedgerows by the plough. If one follows a January trail it seldom deviates towards the hedge, as it would if a fox were hunting. Rather it indicates that the fox is only interested in getting from one point to another and that this man-provided, flat-bottomed, ready-made track is physically the easiest way of getting there. A further advantage to the fox when it uses the 'dead furrow' may be the protection it affords from the wind and enemies, precious little of which is to be had from either in the middle of a ten-acre ploughed field.

So the Kent's Green foxes in the winter and early spring at least keep to field margins—not a very startling conclusion perhaps, but when one is looking for fox trails and droppings as I was, this knowledge does save a great deal of walking time.

The trails so far mentioned are merely series of footprints recorded in wet earth and are usually the only types one can attribute solely to the local foxes. Trails through thick hedges (Plate 4a) will be used by a number of animals but if one keeps a sharp eye on the vegetation around the gap one can often distinguished between loose hairs of badgers, hares and foxes, the three most likely species to use such a highway. As will be explained later in the chapter on Diet, the hairs of most British mammals can be positively identified by using simple microscope techniques.

Fox trails through vegetation can only be identified for certain during the late spring and summer. Mowing grass fields are particularly productive of trails; these are narrow and marked only by the grass being bent over in the direction of travel. Such trails will often be found to lead to a well-flattened circular area, a yard or two in diameter and on the trodden grass will be found feathers, bones and droppings, indicating that the fox has recently used the area as a feeding place. This sort of trail is particularly common around breeding earths in June and July and many are made by the cubs (Plate 4b).

In the summer of 1966, Clewes' field, next to the Pond earths, was ringed by fox trails which also crossed the field of mowing grass. On one occasion, and only because it was taking great leaps as it ran through long grass, I saw a cub crossing this field; presumably it was trying to keep an eye on me as I stood at the edge of the field. On another occasion an adult fox came barging across the same field and only saw me (I was walking) when we were about three yards apart. In this case the fox could not have picked up my scent and the rustle of the grass presumably prevented it from hearing me, and vice versa. Most of the field trails away from the margins seemed to be used only once, the cubs making a fresh trail each time they crossed a field. Well-marked, regular highways of trodden grass were found all the way round the outside of the mowing grass field, indicating that this was the most frequently used route from one side to another.

Dew Trails

On sunny mornings after a heavy dew, I have sometimes picked up a fox trail in grassland. The fox's feet dislodge the droplets of water from individual grass blades and give a dark green, bruised look to each, thus producing a well-marked trail that can easily be seen if viewed against the sun. The possibility of following such trails is, of course, dependent upon the extent of the grassland. On the Kent's Green land, the grassland was not extensive enough to allow dew trails to be followed far, and in any case they were usually found just cutting off a field corner and disappearing into the hedge. I did, however, find them useful in plotting routes used by the foxes and this sometimes led to direct observation of the animal.

Snow Trails

During my years of observation snow fall was never very great and that which fell did not last long. Even so I was able to map out some trails more accurately, and also to locate some bedding places (Fig. 3). Occasionally, during January and February, I have found double fox trails indicating that a pair of foxes have travelled together. On one occasion I discovered what I interpreted as evidence of a court-ship chase; the fox prints were disposed in rough circles which sometimes overlapped and made almost a figure of eight in the snow.

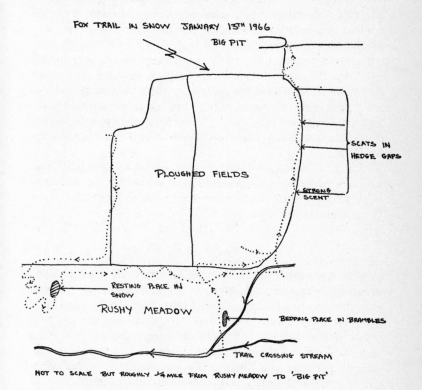

3. Diagram from author's field notebook of a January snow trail

As there was such poor snow on the lowlands of Gloucestershire in the winter of 1965–6, I decided to do some snow tracking on the high ground of the Cotswolds, where the snow fall was more generous and persistent. The Cotswold snow trails gave me two further examples of fox sign that I had not been able to detect at Kent's Green.

The date was 14 January 1966 and there was about six inches of good snow on the floor of the Woodchester Park valley, covering most of the low vegetation and making the ground a hummocky white expanse. Here and there, however, a few bits of scrubby growth did penetrate the white and it seemed that these irregularities which caught my eye were also attractive to the foxes. Each protruding tuft of dead grass or bramble had a few drops of fox urine sprinkled over, giving a yellow stain in the snow. I paced along one trail for a distance of approximately seventy-five feet and counted ten fox urination points; the significance of this activity will be discussed in the chapter on Fox Society.

The second new sign in the Woodchester snow was something I took to be the mark left by the fox's brush; it consisted of a smooth depression shaped like a half cylinder, about a yard long.

Droppings are, of course, easy to find along snow trails, as are remains of meals and places where the fox has dug out rodents, usually field voles, from beneath the protective cover of both snow and long, dead grass.

With patience and good snow, one can discover a great deal about the foxes' nocturnal activities and I much regret that my interest in this type of work had not been aroused in time to take advantage of the memorable winter of 1962–3.

WATER JUMPS

These first became known to me in January 1965, when collecting droppings from a particularly productive trail that closely followed the banks of a small stream—a trail I later called the Rutting Trail. I had noticed that a number of droppings occurred on short side trails which left the main one and appeared to end rather abruptly at the stream, though on closer examination the trails were seen to continue on the other side. There are three of these trails within only a 100-foot stretch of the stream. Each consisted of a scramble down the steep bank on one side (a vertical distance of about four feet) and then a modest jump of about three feet across the stream. There was a very narrow landing platform, only an inch or two wide, at the base of the very steep bank opposite, with again a vertical distance of about four feet to negotiate. Footprints at the water's edge indicated that the fox jumped in one direction only and that these jumps were in constant use from January until late April, after which they seemed to fall out of use. The significance of these jumps in the life of the fox will be discussed in the chapter on Music and Movement.

FOX SCENT

It is extremely difficult for human beings, with their poorly developed sense of smell, to realise that we can never really appreciate unaided a large part of our physical environment, namely the smell of 'things'. Everything has a smell but we only detect objects that possess this property to a high degree. We distinguish between agreeable and disagreeable odours, with a few 'in between' smells we cannot easily classify, and what is pleasant to one individual may be nauseating or repulsive to another. The world of smell being thus largely unknown to us, we must not assume that other animals have the same smell standards as ourselves. This would appear to be self-evident from the way some insects are attracted to objects which smell fetoidal to us.

Animals that hunt and those that are hunted usually have the most efficiently developed sense of smell, and the fox as a hunting animal is no exception to this generalisation. Smells give foxes information about past and contemporary events in their surroundings to an extent that we cannot possibly appreciate. A fox lives in a world full of the scents produced by its normal activities and bodily functions such as urination, defecation and secretions from anal glands. Without early recognition of this fact, we can never begin to understand fox behaviour.

Scent that is recognisable either to ourselves or our dogs is produced at a number of sites on or in the fox's body.

The Foot Gland

This is a deep glandular pit, present on all feet, which opens in front of the plantar pad and is marked by a small region of naked skin which can be seen when the digits are extended (Fig. 4). The scent produced by this gland leaves a foot trail which might be of importance to the fox in retracing its steps, should this be necessary. It can, of course, be followed by other animals, to the disadvantage of the fox.

The Sub-caudal Glands

As the name implies, these are situated at the root of and beneath

25

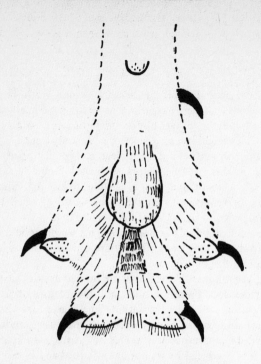

4. Fox forefoot with digits extended to
expose the foot gland (after Pocock)

the tail adjacent to and on either side of the anus. The scent produced
by these glands is extremely pungent and readily detected by the
human nose. Liberation of scent does not seem to be under the conscious control of the fox but is produced rather as a reaction to
fright. The function of such a smell in some animals, the skunk for
example, is to deter a would-be aggressor; in others, it is a form of
social signal to warn members of the species of imminent danger. I
think this unlikely in the case of the fox.

There are two other scent-producing areas, the first of which, the
general body surface, is probably of little significance. The skin produces oily secretions which help to keep it soft and healthy. The
function of the last area or tail 'gland' I do not know. This is a small
area on the dorsal surface of the tail about three inches from its root
(Plate 5a). It is marked by a tuft of black hair, the gland itself being

a small bare patch about the size of a sixpence. Linnaeus, it seems, thought that an ambrosial odour diffused from this gland and suggested that it counteracted odour produced from the sub-caudal gland. This gland is present in other members of the dog family, *Canidae*, but is particularly well developed in the fox.

Lionel Edwards (1949) mentions a saying that a frightened fox gives off most smell. Talbot (1966) reports that the faster a fox is kept moving the better the scent and that a sinking fox leaves little scent. Why the fox produces so much scent when being chased is not an easy question to answer. It may well be a fright reaction, as Edwards suggests.

While both sexes have sub-caudal glands, it is often claimed that these are larger in the male; I have no evidence to bring forward, but this seems highly probable.

Scenting Posts

Often when walking around the fox trails a sudden strong smell of fox has caused me to stop and try to determine the source. In my sniffings, I have been led to a gate-post, a pile of brushwood, or even to a slightly raised large stone, and at these places the fox scent has been intense. These scenting posts may also be urination places and are often in regular use, seeming to act as a focus of activity for the local fox population. A fox or domestic dog can gain a great deal of information from sniffing, eventually adding its own contribution at the scenting post or lamp post. The animals learn what others of their own species are in the area, also about the presence and breeding condition of members of the opposite sex. They may also detect more subtle details, such as the physical and even mental state of previous visitors. A fox may well be a stranger to the area and the resident foxes may be able to detect, in the urine smell, the fear the stranger displays on finding itself in unfamiliar and therefore potentially hostile surroundings.

There is a marked increase in the use of scenting posts in December and January; they then seem to be very important and it is at this time of year that the rut is most intense. Scenting probably takes place throughout the year but I have only actually watched a fox performing this operation in September (chapter on Fox Society).

Urination and scenting, although they probably often take place at the same time, are really two separate activities. Urination occurs when the fox's bladder is emptied and the smell associated with the process is the smell of the urine. One form of scenting involves the use of the sub-caudal glands which produce the characteristic fox smell and which also help to give the faeces a similar odour. This aspect of the fox's life will be dealt with more fully in the chapter on Fox Society. Suffice it to say at present that we can detect fox smell and that it is a very important field sign.

FAECES

There is, in polite society, no commonly used word which adequately covers animals' anal evacuations. Otters are said to produce spraints, deer fewmets; rabbits and hares produce marbles but there are few other examples of animal's droppings which have special names. We tend to use such words as droppings, excrements or faeces as general terms but the American term 'scats' is, I think, a useful short one and is used throughout the rest of this book.

Fox scats are similar in general appearance to those produced by dogs and this introduces a complication when one is trying to collect fox droppings from an area with a high dog population. To combat this I always noted when and where I saw dog footprints and in which fields my farmer neighbour had recently worked with his attendant dog—by so doing I was able to avoid collecting from dogs' trails. I found that, contrary to what is usually thought, foxes did deposit scats on man-made roadways and that roads could not therefore be ignored. Whenever I was in doubt about the origin of a scat I found that those from a fox could usually be distinguished by the characteristic 'tail' formed by the drawing out of one or both ends of the passage and consisting of prey hair or grass blades. There is also the characteristic foxy odour of fresh fox scats which, together with their general composition, helps identification. There are often two or three typically shaped sections in one fox evacuation and if all the pieces found obviously belonged together I analysed them as a single scat. Usually, however, I found only a single section which, again, I called a single scat for analysis purposes. The quantity of material in each scat depended upon the type of meal the fox had eaten. After a fruit meal, the scats have a typical fox shape but this is soon lost as rain, wind, fungi and insects begin their work of disintegration. When much animal hair is present, the scat will often remain on the ground for some considerable time without losing its shape. These are the scats which are usually collected unless the area is regularly patrolled to make sure that fruit scats and others of a less permanent nature are not overlooked. There is a risk that the importance of animal prey to a fox may be exaggerated if only 'typical' fox scats are collected, and by collecting scats at least once a week I was able to estimate fairly accurately the age of those I found.

A mucus coat to a carnivore's scat seems to be fairly typical and it has been suggested that the mucus facilitates the movement of broken, sharp-edged bones down the intestine of the animal. The otter certainly produces a good mucus coat on its spraints, probably in this case to prevent the fish bones from damaging the gut. For the fox, however, I seldom found a good mucus coat, except on scats containing bird remains. It may be that the fox reacts to sharp bird bones in the same way as the otter appears to react to fish bones. Another common characteristic of fox scats containing bird remains is the chalky white colour which seems to be due to the partial dissolving of the bird bones in the gut of the fox, which produces a yellow-white chalky sludge. When a fox scat does have a mucus coat, this seldom lasts long as it is quickly removed by soil, insects and rain. The intensity of foxy smell about a scat varies with the contents, being least in a fruit scat and greatest in one with feathers.

Collection of fox scats in the autumn was aided by the occurrence of a halo of fungal threads surrounding each fresh deposit—this was also useful in ageing. I covered the area on foot at least once a week during the three years of the study, as well as tramping laboriously over many miles of ploughed field and grazing land. I concentrated my search on field margins and these proved to be the most productive areas, particularly in autumn and winter. A sharp look-out was always kept for fox trails and on a number of occasions while following these I was able to sniff out scats. Gaps in hedges, old tree stumps, bare or burnt ground, cow dung and even salt licks, together with remains of animals, were all investigated and I found that foxes seemed to prefer these areas in which to deposit their scats.

The occurrence of scats on dead birds, particularly on feathers, and upon patches of ground where hedge trimmings had been burnt at a short distance from field margins, was most marked. Foxes regularly visited these areas, as did the local hares, and scats from both animals were commonly found associated.

Excavated runway systems of woodmice and voles often had a scat deposited beside them to prove the doer of the deed. This was particularly well marked in September 1965, near woodmouse tunnels,

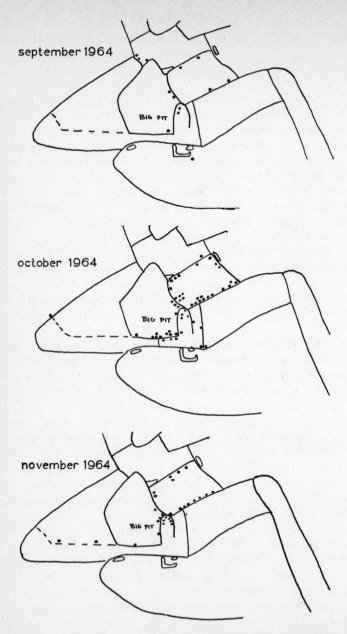

september 1964

october 1964

november 1964

5a. Distribution of fox scats in the Big Pit area, September 1964 to November 1964

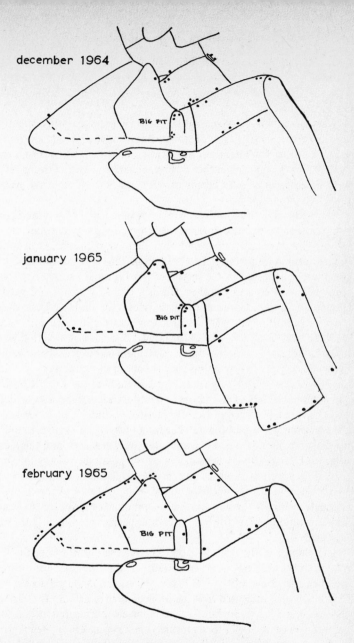

december 1964

BIG PIT

january 1965

BIG PIT

february 1965

BIG PIT

5b. Distribution of fox scats in the Big Pit area,
December 1964 to February 1965

c

and is a commonly observed field sign of fox in the autumn. In late summer and early autumn many fox scats were collected in a few days from man-made roadways—in this case foresters' trails outside my study area.

Scats can often be found on tussocks of grass or other slightly elevated areas, such as a pile of stones. But while such slight elevations seem to attract fox attention, the location of scat sites tends to vary from season to season; in fact during the late spring they were very difficult indeed to find whereas at other times they occurred every few yards around a field.

Fox scats were found to recur in a particular place for a week or two and then were not deposited there, becoming concentrated elsewhere. These concentrations and other signs were most conspicuous in late autumn and winter. The autumn of 1964 was noteworthy for the number collected in the region of Big Pit natal earth. Sixty-five scats were collected in October within a radius of about 100 yards (Fig 5a). This may represent the activity of a fox family which, after being born in Big Pit that year, probably returned to their birth site just before the final break up of the family. A similar observation was made by Scott (1943) in the United States and he believes that the old natal dens act as rallying points for the cubs in the autumn. Again, in the November of 1964, sign was concentrated around Big Pit Earth but not so intensely; I found only twenty-six scats in an area which had produced sixty-five in October. Distribution of scats in December was even wider and the number found was again smaller than in the previous month. The area was intensively searched and the lack of ground cover should have increased the possibility of my finding scats if they were present. I consider the reduction in numbers to be significant of a change in the habits of the local foxes. Autumn high correlates with a known maximum weight of adult foxes for the year and is a time of plentiful fruit, which appeared prominently in the scat analysis.

The change in the scat distribution over the months is probably related to the autumn break up and dispersal of the fox cubs during October and November. The snow tracking I managed to do in December 1964 indicated that the immediate area around the earths was not in great use. In January, scats were concentrated at first on the margins of one field, then another, and occurred most frequently in or near gaps in hedges. While scats can be found in this position at other times of the year, their January occurrence in these places is, I feel, more than fortuitous and related to the rut that is in full swing in January. (Fig 5b).

Cub scats, which are of the same general shape as the adult's but smaller, were mostly collected from earths or from play areas (Plate 5b). Again it was noticeable, even with cubs, how scats are often deposited on the remains of prey.

FOOD CACHES AND DIGS

Foxes, like badgers, will when the occasion demands dig out small animals, particularly worms and small mammals. A badger dig or 'snuffle hole' is quite a characteristic sign, mainly because of the use this animal makes of its snout. Examination of these digs leads me to believe that the badger makes the initial dig, perhaps for a worm that has tried to retreat down its hole. The snout is then brought into use and pushes down into the soft earth so that the incisor teeth can grip the retreating worm. This pushing of the snout leaves one smooth, almost polished, side to the small excavation.

A fox, although it sometimes digs up worms, more usually confines its digging to excavating small mammals, particularly field voles. The latter often make shallow tunnel systems just beneath the roots of grass and these are easy enough to discover if one goes to any rough pasture that has been neglected for some years. It is only necessary to part the long grass to get down to the soil surface and there, often around the base of coarse grass, will be a well-marked grass tunnel which will be found eventually to disappear just below soil level. Occasionally, collections of dry grass will be found in these runway systems and mark either the breeding nest where the young voles are born, or the adult voles' temporary home. It is these nests that are dug out by the fox, who locates them either by scent or sound, or a combination of both. It is quite common to come across a roughly excavated vole runway and to find the remains of the nest together, sometimes, with a few bits of fur from the late owner. After eating the vole, the fox often defecates near the excavation, so leaving for us another sign. Field voles are not the only mammals to be dug out by foxes, woodmice and moles sometimes suffer the same fate.

When there is an abundance of food, a common habit of the fox is to bury or cache some of it. At Ravenglass in Cumberland, Niko Tinbergen found that the local foxes buried black-headed gulls' eggs in sand dunes during May when they were plentiful and dug them up again in July. Adult gulls were killed and also buried, or at least partly concealed in vegetation. By burying hens' eggs in the sand, Tinbergen was able to show that a fox could locate these even after three months of being buried in shifting sand. On the land I studied, I only once found a food cache and that was of a tawny owl half buried in dead leaves not far from the earths around Clewes' Pond. This sign is, however, quite characteristic and worth looking for.

In the literature about fox feeding habits in other countries there are frequent references to the caching habit, particularly in snow. Sande (1943) once found a cache containing a hare, ten field mice and a grouse.

From studying the fox sign as indicated, I was able during the first two years of my study to obtain a picture, albeit a rough one, of the activities of Kent's Green foxes. I was able to establish that there was a fox population and that it was active in the area I had chosen to study. By reading the sign, I was able to map out the major highways used by the foxes; hedge gaps used by them were plotted as were the defecation points; in fact, all locations that were of importance to the local foxes.

During the first six months I saw only a fleeting glimpse of a living fox, as it was not my aim at that time to observe them directly; I did not know how to set about this task and felt I could make best use of the limited time I had available for the study by concentrating on sign, since this seemed to be affording much useful information.

During the spring of 1964 I was able to watch a fox family in Big Pit, and after this experience my horizons widened. I was no longer content to find out about the animal indirectly though, as I soon found, direct observation presented much greater problems than did the discovery of feeding habits. How I tackled these problems is the subject of the next chapter.

Watching
Foxes

Success in watching foxes in the field depends on a number of factors, not least the observer's patience. Another important factor is the amount of activity shown by the fox at the particular time of year when one is watching. Daytime activity varies tremendously with time of year and sex of the fox, as I discovered only after many hours of often fruitless observations at all times of day and night throughout the year. Each time I saw a fox I noted time, place, wind direction, the fox's path and, if possible, a physical description of the animal. After nearly three years of doing this, I have been able to establish a rough fox-activity pattern and I now know approximately the times of day foxes are likely to be active and therefore observable. This saves me many hours of fruitless waiting and increases the chances of watching foxes going about their normal activities.

A knowledge of the local fox highways and foraging grounds—as discussed in the previous chapter—is an essential preliminary to any really serious watching. Given that, the remaining requirement, equipment, is probably the simplest of all to meet. I use an old pair of 6 × 50 binoculars which give me quite good night visibility, and have a dull black finish to the case, without any bright metallic parts to reflect light and so give away the observer's position. Another item, and in summer almost more important than the first, is a good fly repellent to be used on all exposed parts of the body. No matter how good one's self-control, it is almost impossible, and most undesirable, to sit still for hours in a mosquito-infested spot without some chemical aid. For summer clothing, I wear a lightweight green anorak and green or brown trousers, with a pair of soft, lightweight brown shoes that enable me to 'feel' the ground I cover rather than merely walk across it. I never wear a hat, although I often think I should so that the outline of my face would be broken and so add to concealment.

We now have to get into a good position for watching, with as wide a field of view as possible. The vantage point may be a branch of a tree, the top of a field gate, the earth bank at the side of a pond, or just a piece of high ground where one can sit against a tree. Artificial hides can, of course, be erected but I consider these are only really worth setting up at breeding earths. For general observations, one needs to know a number of natural vantage points around the area from which to make a quick choice after considering wind direction and the expected approach route of the fox. Whichever vantage point is chosen must be comfortable and allow the observer to sit completely still for two hours or more at a time, without some part of his anatomy 'going to sleep'. This is not only uncomfortable when the 'awakening' begins but can also be dangerous if trying to descend from a high perch on a dark night.

My approach to a viewing point is always calculated to avoid crossing the track I expect the fox to follow. Human scent lingers long in footprints, or even on bruised grass, and a fox will not happily cross a fresh human trail; one an hour or two old is still fresh to a vulpine nose.

Having selected, carefully approached and settled down to watch, my next step is to familiarise myself with the immediate surrounding features, noting which bushes might look 'fox like' in poor light and which clump of grass might resemble a sitting fox when one is hoping so intensely to see one there. An hour looking through binoculars in poor light can lead one to imagine that almost any irregularity on the ground is a fox. A clump of ox-eye daisies on the far side of a field, a few strands of hay or a single large thistle standing in a pasture can all cause optical illusions which may take the form of the fox. If one knows what is where, this hazard will be minimised, though never completely countered. Also, a new shape appearing in an area that is being carefully scanned is more likely to be detected if one has a detailed knowledge of the surroundings. Many times I have only detected a fox by noting that a visible shape was not there the last time I looked at that spot. This training of the eye is a point I would emphasise with any would-be fox watcher.

Fox activity is characterised by an almost continuous rapid and jerky movement, particularly when hunting. This feature helps me to detect foxes in poor light and if a suspected fox shape does not move within ten seconds I usually reckon it is not a fox.

And after all this, what does one actually see? Usually, my observations are confined to a very few minutes, though sometimes I have been fortunate enough to enjoy half an hour or more of continuous watching. Such occasions, however, are few and far between.

A second form of approach to fox watching is the mobile one, and the longer I watch foxes the more I am convinced that this is a more rewarding method, except when cub watching at an earth. All that is necessary is to walk slowly and quietly around the known fox haunts; by doing just this I have had some of my longest spells of fox watching.

There is yet another way of watching foxes, and this is by using artificial light. It has been suggested that some animals could be followed on their nightly walks by using a red light with a good beam, since nocturnal animals are not very sensitive to light at this end of the spectrum. I am not convinced that this technique could be used to follow foxes at night, although it may well be a possibility in trailing badgers. The method I use to watch foxes at their earths is very simple and one that I discovered quite by accident.

In the autumn of 1965 I started to experiment in the use of red torchlight for watching foxes emerging from earths in Big Pit. My first very primitive attempt was to set up on a convenient field boundary post a powerful torch showing a red light above the earth. By adjusting the beam of the torch I was able to focus this upon the entrance to an earth I knew to be in use. Whether my activities above the earth made the fox suspicious I do not know, but within about half an hour of my first sitting alongside my torch and looking down the side of the pit at the earth, there was a sudden sound of displaced marl sliding and rolling to the bottom of the slope; the fox that had precipitated this minor marl-slide rushed out of its shelter and was gone into the darkness. The next time I repeated the experiment I arrived about half an hour before it began to get dark, placed my torch on the same post but this time retired with my binoculars to the tree that overhung Big Pit on the far side away from Slope Earth. As it became darker, so my narrow shaft of red light became more obvious; however, despite the use of binoculars the illumination was not sufficient and whilst at times I thought I could see a fox's head in the earth's entrance, this never actually materialised.

Deciding that there was little future in this sort of observation unless I was able to provide a much more powerful source of light, I removed the red glass and some days later took the torch with me to guide me safely into a new position very close to Slope Earth. I hoped that, with binoculars trained on the hole, I would be able to watch the fox emerge without light. The first night without the red light was successful; in the dim evening light at 6.15 on 17 February I was able to distinguish the familiar shape of a fox as it slowly and quietly emerged, hesitated slightly and then climbed the side of the pit to the field above, only the slight patter of dislodged marl breaking the silence. This fox had a very prominent white tip to its tail and I very much doubt if I would have picked up the shape had not my attention been drawn to this moving white blaze.

The next evening I again took up my position in the tree roots about ten feet away from and slightly above the earth. It was raining and there was so much sound of water dripping from the trees that I was not particularly quiet in my approach. Crawling in poor light along wet, algae-covered roots, carrying a heavy torch and a pair of binoculars, does not increase the possibility of arriving silently at one's destination. Darkness had fallen by the time I was in position, although it was still only 6 pm; if the fox was going to be consistent in its emergence time, it was not due for another fifteen minutes or so. The rain was now falling heavily, I was becoming very wet and beginning to question the whole expedition, including my own sanity. In such situations one tends to act on impulse and, convinced that I would see nothing, I switched on the torch, directing a powerful beam of white light on to the entrance to the earth. I sat there for a few minutes contemplating my folly and the illuminated earth, when to my amazement a fox's head appeared in the part of the tunnel thrown into light by the beam of the torch. Not only appeared, but came to the entrance of the earth and with ears flat back, slightly submissively, looked directly at the light before slowly ducking down again into the tunnel. A few moments later it came forward again and, with its head and shoulders out of the earth and its fore paws on the rim of the entrance, half sat, bathed in torchlight, for what seemed to me a very long time. The fox then slowly pulled the rest of its long body and white-tipped tail from the earth and gradually made its way up the side of the pit.

I sat dripping wet but very still for a further ten minutes or so before retracing my slippery path back to the field. It had not been possible for me to look at my watch when the fox first appeared but it must have been at almost the same time—6.15—as on the previous dry and much lighter evening. Now I knew that one could watch foxes—or at least this fox—by white light.

Since then I have watched foxes on a number of occasions at both Big Pit and Savage's Little Pond Earth, and at the latter a vixen emerged at about the same time night after night, despite the torchlight. I checked to see whether the light made any difference to the emergence time and found that it did not.

It would seem from these and other observations at earths, that if a fox wants to leave it will do so rather than wait until any unusual features of its surroundings are restored to normal, as badgers seem to prefer to do. When I have been watching badgers and turned the same white torchlight on to a set the badger may take a quick look out of the hole and sniff at the illuminated earth, but he will then duck down again and either emerge from another hole or 'stay put' underground. True, badgers will become accustomed to white light and have even been filmed at night by this technique, but a badger takes a long time to get used to a change in its environment and displays flight reaction until long experience has shown that the change does not of itself bring danger.

The fox's reaction to the same novel situation seems to be less stereotyped, in that flight reaction is not produced unless it detects a known danger signal, for example, the smell of man associated with the new object or change in its environment. I suspect that if the Slope Earth fox had caught a whiff of my scent when the light was turned on to the earth there would have been a rapid retreat and the next night the light was used, even if no human smell was conveyed to the fox, it would have shown the same fear reaction because it associated light with danger. This ability to correlate quickly two or more apparently unrelated phenomena is what I understand as intelligent behaviour in an animal and, to this extent, a fox is to me a more intelligent creature than a badger.

THE ACTIVITY PATTERN

By using these various direct methods of fox watching I was able to obtain some idea of the foxes' activity at different times of the year. Added to direct watching, I also used evidence of times of barking to give some indication of times of emergence and activity.

I have attempted to combine the evidence from the many observations made by various direct and indirect methods, and have drawn them together month by month. It must be remembered, however, that while these observations span three complete years, they refer only to Gloucestershire foxes, unless otherwise indicated. The activity of the foxes I have studied may be directly applicable to other areas, but I have no proof of this. The available literature on the Scottish fox suggests that its breeding season is roughly four weeks later than that of the fox in southern England, so it seems reasonable to suppose that the whole of the Scottish fox's life history is approximately a month out of phase, or later than that now to be described.

January

Fox watching in this month is a cold, often wet and very unrewarding occupation so far as direct observation of the animals is concerned. Mine have been limited to rear or, at best, side views of retreating animals I have disturbed from their resting places, for surface living seems to be the general rule at this time of the year, at least for dog foxes. During my field walks in 1966 I three times disturbed foxes, one from a grassy bank above Big Pit, another from a thick hedge near Rushy Meadow and a third from a pollarded willow leaning out across a small stream. On each occasion the day was sunny and the foxes presumably were taking advantage of the solar energy, so conserving some of their own. Foxes can sometimes be seen moving about and feeding in broad daylight in January and their general activity seems to be spread over the whole twenty-four hours rather than being confined to nocturnal perambulations.

It was during this month that, by regular evening listening and plotting on a large-scale map the positions of all the barks heard, I was able to map out roughly what I called barking trails of foxes with distinctive voices. This work involved me in many hours of standing and walking or, as I later tried, driving slowly round the lanes with windows open and stopping frequently to plot the positions of the barking foxes. I always used the same route and soon became familiar with the places and times at which each fox barked.

The trail of one particular fox that I called the 'wo-wo' fox from its typical deep, staccato, rasping bark, became particularly well known to me. This animal based its barking activity on Clewes' Farm Earth and began to bark each evening for some weeks just as the milking machine was started up in a shed opposite the earth and only separated from it by the pond.

The 'wo-wo' fox seemed to be roused to vocal activity by the noise of the machine and usually barked at the entrance to its earth for a few minutes before setting off on its trail, barking as it moved along. The route taken was roughly the same each evening, much of it through orchard and about three-quarters of a mile in length, so that the animal could be followed quite easily by ear.

Deciding to try and obtain a recording of this fox, I set up a portable tape-recorder in a shed opposite the earth one evening and waited. The motor of the milking machine was switched on at the usual time but, for the first time for weeks, the fox did not bark. Night after night I tried but always drew a blank, so I changed my tactics and decided to follow the fox, which was still performing its nightly barking around but not at the earth. It was a damp, misty evening when I carefully made my way to the far side of the field containing the pond with its earth. I had not long to wait before I heard the familiar 'wo-wo' coming from the orchard that bounded two sides of the field in which I was sitting. The fox, I gathered from its barks, was moving up the hedge towards me and as the 'wo-wo's' grew louder I switched on the recorder, but after two or three more barks all was silent save for the droning of the milking machine and the occasional clang of a milk churn. While I sat there, the fox must have made its way past me until it was slightly above in the sloping field, for just as I was about to walk back to the milking shed there was an extremely loud 'wo-wo' from only a few yards away. The recorder was still at my feet so I had to bend down quickly to switch on, and, with the microphone held far too close to the motor for good recording, I was able to record four of the loudest 'wo-wo's' imaginable. The fox must have stopped in its tracks to deliver this vocal broadside at me from a distance of no more than ten yards.

I managed to record this fox on a number of other occasions in January and though barking can be best heard on frosty, still even-

41

ings, weather conditions seem to have little effect on fox activity; barking can be heard on even wild, wet nights if one takes the trouble to go out and listen.

The foxes in general usually began to bark at about 6 pm, regardless of weather conditions, although they could be much more easily heard on still, frosty nights than in windy, drizzly conditions. (See list of barking times in Appendix A.) Until 9 pm activity was intense, after which barking was only sporadic and finally petered out at about 11 o'clock.

To try and simplify my task of recording fox-barking times, I bought a simple 'baby-alarm' system and installed the microphone in a tree at the bottom of the garden. This enabled me to record from the comfort of an armchair the times at which barks were produced. On hearing a fox, and noting the time, I would go out into the lanes and determine its barking position, sometimes following it on foot along the stream valleys. Another advantage of this method was that when I was away from home in the evenings, my wife could record the type of barks heard and so provide much valuable information.

Visual evidence, therefore, indicates that foxes at this time of year are living on the surface and are active most of the twenty-four hours, while barking evidence tells us that evening activity is at its peak between 6 and 9 pm.

The fox trails I followed were mostly a yard or so from the hedge or field margin, and usually ran along the dead furrow in ploughed fields. I noticed few signs of deviation from the furrow and little evidence of food remains or attempts to obtain food. The general impression I got from the multitude of trails around almost every field in my area was of great, restless activity among the local fox population, who appeared to put movement at a premium and feeding very much as a secondary consideration. This is reflected, I think, in the lack of droppings at the beginning of the month.

Although I did find a few scats on tussocks of grass beside the field trails, it was not until near the end of the month that fox sign became intense on what I have called the Rutting Trail. I first noticed this well-trodden main fox highway at the end of November 1965 when I collected four droppings from it, all of which had been deposited in very conspicuous positions. During the following December and early January the trail, which ran alongside the small stream draining Rushy Meadow, was well used by the local foxes but very few droppings occurred on it. On 11 January, after a slight fall of snow, I detected evidence of what I considered to be a fox mating, but it was not until the 24th that really large concentrations of fox sign appeared along the trail.

At many points I found fresh scats associated with gaps in the nearby hedge, obviously gateways used by the local foxes as through-routes. So common were scats near hedge gaps that I systematically investigated each gap along the hedge and almost invariably found scats after a few seconds' search. The quantity of scat found in each case was rarely large and I was left with the impression that the fox had almost rationed them out so that as many gaps as possible would be covered along this trail.

This activity continued for a week or so, after which only an occasional dropping was found along the trail, although it was still well used, as evidenced by the number of fresh footprints. This fox habit of marking first one stretch of trail intensively for a few days and then concentrating on a new one, possibly in an adjoining field, is, to my mind, now well established.

The placing of scats in gaps in hedges is typical of winter activity, particularly in January. Moreover, in addition to the scats on the trail, intense fox smell was noticed during the latter part of January and I located a large number of scenting posts within a very short distance.

The Rushy Meadow trail was little used after the breeding season and it was for this reason, and because of the intensity of use during the rut, that I called it the Rutting Trail (Fig 6). I had noticed other trails of this nature in previous years and I think that the intense marking is an expression of the territorial activities of the local fox population.

The water jumps already described are a feature of rutting trails that follow the course of a stream, as many do, and were used by the foxes to very much the same extent as was the adjacent trail. They continued in use until April, after which they were no longer marked by fox footprints.

During January, there is much activity around the earths, which are used certainly by the vixens and probably only occasionally by the dogs. A few scats can usually be found near or sometimes in the entrances to the earths, but the majority seem to be deposited some little distance away.

In January, the dog fox appears to be mainly a surface dweller, while the vixen still uses the traditional earths in which she passes the

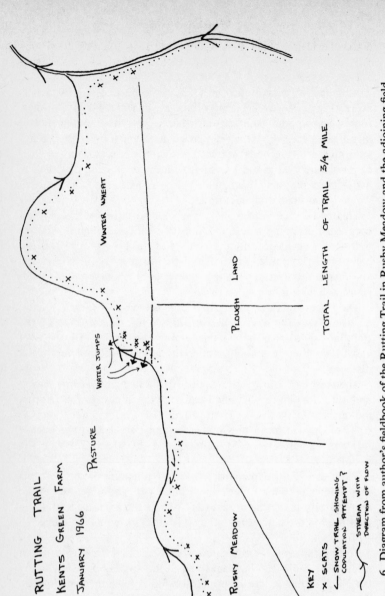

6. Diagram from author's fieldbook of the Rutting Trail in Rushy Meadow and the adjoining field

day, only emerging just after nightfall. These conclusions are supported by evidence obtained during my regular walks at this time of year. I have not seen one of my known vixens on the surface nor have I flushed one from cover. I have flushed some foxes but these were strangers to me, presumably dog foxes. While I cannot claim this evidence to be conclusive of a difference in habit of the sexes, I do believe it might be confirmed if more observations and careful records were kept.

February

After many hours of crouching on the exposed tree roots in Big Pit and Small Pond Earths, I was able to establish that vixens living in these earths emerged between 6 and 6.30 pm every evening, regardless of weather conditions. I knew that adult foxes were active until about 8 am on February mornings, for I was able to watch them returning to their earths at about this time on a number of occasions. My farmer neighbour also saw a number of foxes in the area during daytime, but not so frequently as in January.

My armchair listening for fox calls was continued throughout the month, as well as the more demanding outdoor listening, but little vocal activity was heard. During February 1966 I heard foxes on only three nights. The calls were yells and screams which, on one occasion, sounded like a duck being slowly strangled. I only heard the winter 'wo-wo' type of bark on one occasion.

My white light method of fox watching proved very successful in February 1966, and I was able to make a number of observations at both Big Pit and Small Pond Earths. On February 19 I arrived at Big Pit at 5.50 pm. It was a fairly warm evening but the little wind that channelled down the Pit prevented my sitting in my usual position near Slope Earth, so I made my way round the rim of the Pit and climbed into the branches of a tree projecting over the Look Out Earth. About five minutes after I was comfortably installed a fox appeared from Badger Earth. This was just after 6 pm and the light was still fair when using binoculars. 'White Tip', for it was the vixen I had seen earlier in the month emerge from Slope Earth, made her way to the temporary pond which had formed at the bottom of the marl pit and drank for a few seconds. She then moved to a nearby tree, paused and, I think, urinated, after which, with occasional pauses, she slowly made her way up the side of Big Pit. As she neared the lip of the pit a blackbird's alarm note stopped her short; she crouched for about thirty seconds, then moved off under a nearby gate and was lost to view. After waiting for about five minutes I rose slowly from my perch but even this slight movement disturbed the fox that must still have been foraging unseen a few yards from me. I heard her gallop away down the side of the very wet field nearby, sounding rather like a small pony.

During the night of the 23rd, my neighbour lost a duck and found a goose which had been left beheaded but was otherwise unmarked. The only traces of the duck were white feathers near the farm, so I systematically visited each earth known to me in the hope of finding evidence that one of 'my' foxes had perpetrated the crime. Despite searching all the known hedge tunnels, lying up places and earths no feathers were found, but I was able to establish that all the earths were either in use or had been recently visited and re-excavated. At two of the earths there was intense fox smell and one had a dropping near the entrance.

Apart from earths, there was little field sign of foxes in February. Footprint tracks were found and one of these was a double trail, presumably made by a pair of foxes travelling together. Generally, however, trails and scats were difficult to find even under good tracking conditions. The Rutting Trail was still used but scats were rarely found on it. This lack of field sign and barking activity suggests a much less active period for the local fox population than we saw in January and is, I think, due to the rut having ended and a general slackening in the pace of fox life.

March

The number of earths showing evidence of being used declined, and the few that were in use I took to be those in which the vixens had produced their litters or were about to do so. Small Pond Earth was being used in March 1966 and a good trail led to it from the nearby pasture land. On the 17th, I made my way there on a cold, dull evening with a slight south-east wind. After I had arrived and settled down, the usual evening alarm-note bird chorus began: robins, wrens, rooks, magpies and later blackbirds, pheasants and partridges all contributed in their characteristic ways. Normally at that time of evening—about 6.15 pm—bird song was slight and one usually heard only wrens and blackbirds.

At 7.10 pm, when it was very nearly dark, a fox emerged cautiously from the earth, stayed around the entrance for about a minute and then made off, snapping a twig as it went. I would not have seen the animal, even with binoculars, had it not been for the prominent long white tip to the tail which I recognised as belonging to the vixen I had last seen in Big Pit a week earlier.

The slight noise made by the retreating vixen did not appear to disturb two moorhens which had settled for the night on the very full pond, but immediately I moved there came the moorhen's usual sharp warning note and I wondered just how different a twig snapped by a human foot sounds to a moorhen, compared with one cracked by a fox!

The following evening, 18 March, at 7.5 pm, the vixen emerged into my white torchlight without seeming concerned and, as on the previous night, moved away towards Grange Earth. On the 19th, a much lighter evening, my vixen emerged at 7.20 pm. Her ears first became visible in the torchlight around her earth; then the head came briefly into view before she ducked down again into the hole. For about a minute she bobbed up and down then emerged to look briefly at the light source and sniff at the shadow edge of the beam. She then turned, made a slight noise down into the earth and, with a bound, was up on the bank and away. She paused briefly in the field to look back towards the light and apparently satisfied that all was well, trotted away towards Grange Earth.

I returned to the cottage but was later to hear fox howls in the distance and a short 'yodel' call. The yodel and the yells were the only fox calls heard in March. The significance of these various fox noises is discussed in a later chapter.

Daytime observations on foxes in March are very few and far between. I saw only one fox on the surface in daylight during my study and that was a large animal I disturbed from a surface bed in Three Oaks Pit at the beginning of March 1964.

Trail activity in March seemed to be somewhat sporadic; some days I would find quite marked field sign in the form of scent and scats, the latter placed fairly prominently on tussocks of grass at the edges of fields but, significantly I think, not near gaps in hedges as they had been in January. Scats were not easy to find in large numbers and it seemed as though the foxes were no longer using them as trail markers, as they had done in January.

Over the whole month, fox activity in the area seemed to be much reduced. The vixens were now confined to their earths by day with their newly-born cubs and the dog foxes seemed either to leave the area or else lie up to recover from the rut.

April

It was again difficult in April to find much field evidence of fox activities. Footprints and scats were occasionally found but only after much close searching. Trail activity declined so much that I often thought the foxes had left my area altogether, until observations of earths showed this was not the case.

On the 6 April 1965 I was watching at Small Pond Earth when the white-tipped vixen emerged at 8.40 pm in good light. She was followed to the entrance of the earth by two cubs, neither of which stayed long after stretching their necks in an effort to see in which direction their mother had gone. They were about five weeks old and it was obvious that the vixen was still kennelling with her cubs at this stage. I saw a similar performance the following evening, the vixen again emerging and being followed by the two cubs who soon retreated back into the earth and did not reappear. In 1964 I had not seen cubs of a similar age until the 24th of the month, this time at Big Pit. Again, the vixen was kennelling with the cubs but that year I saw the cubs emerge a few minutes after the vixen—between 8 and 8.40 pm. She quickly left the area of the earth and immediately began foraging along the hedges in the surrounding fields, returning to her cubs about an hour later for a brief visit, presumably to bring food.

In April, therefore, we have the cubs born in the previous month taking their first look at the world. The vixens at Kent's Green lived with their offspring, in the daytime at least, until the end of the month.

May

It was easier in May each year to watch both adults and cubs in daylight than during any subsequent month. It was, however, a difficult month in which to find field sign. Fox trails and scats were not often found at field margins, and this suggested change of habits was supported by direct observations of the adults. The vixens were frequently seen crossing fields and open spaces which, a few weeks before, they would have skirted, keeping to the usual winter and spring hedge-side trails. This change was probably due, at least in part, to the increase in vegetation, for it was now possible for a fox to 'freeze' in the long grass of an open meadow with a good chance of remaining undetected.

Adult scats, on the rare occasions they were found, occurred in

48

none too obvious spots and did not seem to play such an important part in fox communications as they had in previous months, particularly in winter.

I was able to watch cubs playing around their earths at most times of the day, provided I made a fairly quiet approach. They did not take very much notice of a human observer and even if they ran for cover as I approached, they would soon reappear. Contrary to popular belief, I found no evidence that the adult lies up a little away from the cubs to warn them of approaching danger. Vixens, at least, kennel some distance away from the cubs in May and spend much of the daylight hours searching for food. On many occasions I saw the vixen going to and from the cubs in daylight and was able to work out a rough feeding time-table from observations on two vixens—'White Tip' and another I called 'Buff Tip' after its characteristic tail tag. 'Buff Tip' had her cubs at Clewes' Pond Earth in 1966 and visited them as follows:

1   An early morning visit which usually lasted about half an hour from about 6.15 to 6.45 am. I did not see food being brought, though some may have been regurgitated to the cubs. In early May I suspect this visit is to suckle the cubs and several times I saw the cubs run out to meet the vixen, and on two occasions watched her suckle one cub briefly.

2   The second visit took place in the afternoon between 3.30 and 6.30 pm, but the time was much less consistent than either the early or last visits.

3   At about 8 pm the vixen again visited the cubs, but this time the main purpose seemed to be to move the cubs some distance from the earth to a playing area from which she brought them back about half an hour later. My observations on vixens and cubs are described in other sections of this book.

What the vixen did between these visits I do not know, but she always appeared from the same direction and I assume she was kennelling on the surface somewhere. When coming to the cubs, she never took a circuitous route but always approached directly across the open fields and so was easily observed. What dog foxes do in May is unknown to me but my observations at earths showed that they do not feed the cubs, at least during daylight hours.

I have heard cubs barking in May and their barks are of the 'wo-

49

wo' type. The only adult noises were single yells which appeared to be warning cries.

June

The number of visits by the vixen to the cubs during daylight was very much reduced and, towards the end of the month, ceased altogether. I seldom saw cubs above ground before dusk. My walks in the evenings often brought me more or less face to face with cubs as they wandered by themselves, often some distance from their home earths. It was obvious that the cubs no longer waited for the vixen to arrive before leaving the immediate surroundings of the earth. The cubs emerged late in the evening, between 9.30 and 10 pm, and I sometimes saw them returning alone just before 7 am. Here we had the beginnings of the solitary existence so typical of the adult fox. In April and May, the cubs were sometimes moved from one earth to another but this only happened once as a direct result of human activity. A clay pigeon shoot took place in Big Pit in April 1964 and the family were moved to a new earth the following night. Apart from this, human interference in the form of myself seemed to have little effect on the vixens, which did not move their cubs after I had disturbed them, although I frequently did so by accident.

In June, however, the cubs finally left their earths and took up residence, usually in a thick hedge tangle. They were surface dwellers from then onwards and I was able to find considerable evidence of their activities by investigating overgrown ditches and hedge bottoms. Around the hedges, cub trails soon became prominent, as did remains of food and scats.

Until June, cub playing and general activity was relatively silent, with only an occasional bark or yap. Vocal activity increased greatly in June and I was often able to determine when the cubs were emerging from their hedges by the squealing and screaming noises they made each evening. The cubs were still living as a family group, but were much more independent of the vixen than in previous months.

July

The independence of the cubs became absolute I think, during July and, despite long observations, I did not see either of my well-known vixens visit their offspring, now living in hedges not far from their natal earths. Cub activity was intense and very vocal, particularly just after sunset when, out in the fields each evening, I was able to listen to a chorus of screams and 'tch, tch's' as the cubs fought amongst themselves. Cub play was fast and furious, with a great deal of high leaping and chasing, punctuated by screams. These noises were similar to those I had heard from adults in winter.

Cubs emerged from their hedges between 9 and 9.30 pm. Small foxes wandered about in freshly-cut grass, rushed along trails and pushed cautiously through hedges to see what strange animals the local farmers had turned loose in the next fields. Cub activities soon produced well-marked effects on the local vegetation, particularly in fields of grass. Large areas were flattened, especially at the corners of fields (Plate 4b) near the cubs' dwelling hedge. Numerous trails radiated from the play area which seldom now had food remains, indicating lack of parental support for the cubs, and well-worn trails were established along hedges. After the evening's aggressive play, the cubs seemed to split up in ones and twos and go about their nightly search for small food items, mainly worms and insects. They usually returned to their hedges at about 7.30 am, but I did see cubs still actively moving about at 9.30 one sunny July morning. Still, warm nights at Kent's Green were sometimes broken by an almost hysterical yelling, presumably from the adult foxes—possibly vixens. Most of this yelling occurred in the small hours of full-moon nights. Were the foxes barking at the moon, as they are popularly said to do? More likely, I think that the purpose of the yells is to warn the cubs off the parents' territory as the family breaks up and begins to disperse.

Scats were very difficult to find in July, mainly, I think, because of the foxes' random movements at this time of year. One exception, however, was in July 1965, when I collected a number of scats in a few days from a forest roadway a few miles from my study area.

August

I frequently saw pairs of young foxes playing together and eating fallen fruit in the local orchards. Again, I was able to determine the time of cub activity in the evening from the usual screaming that came from the hedges just around sunset—between 8.30 and 9.15 pm.

Adult fox activity at the beginning of the month seemed to start about 9.30 pm, becoming steadily earlier as the days shortened until, by the end of the month, they were active from 8.30 pm.

Most of my August observations were made as I moved round the area in the late evening, frequently pausing to familiarise myself with each new piece of ground. Cubs as well as adults were watched, and even followed for short distances when the wind was favourable. Adults typically poked about in the long grass of the orchards and I knew from scat analysis that they were consuming large quantities of windfalls, both apples and pears. The cubs I saw were now well grown, but could be distinguished from the adults by their more slender appearance and very thin tails.

Tracking was seldom possible and the only well-marked sign was that of cubs along hedges. I also found a number of lying-up places beyond thick hedge tangles, but there were seldom scats in such locations now. As in the previous month, one man-made trail produced a number of scats for a week or so, after which they no longer occurred.

September

There was much activity just before nightfall by both adults and cubs, beginning about 7.30 pm. At this time I watched adults hunting and also saw pairs of young foxes playing together and feeding in the orchards. On 13 and 14 September 1965, I was able to watch, with binoculars, an adult performing complicated scenting operations in Savage's orchard at 8.30 pm, not long after dark.

Trail activity around the earths now became more obvious and scats occurred quite frequently in the surrounding areas. This month seems to mark the fox's renewed interest in the earths which had been neglected as regular residences since the cubs were moved to the hedge bottoms in June.

Vocal activity was still infrequent, although occasionally and particularly on moonlight evenings, a fox could be heard giving a series of short yells as it moved along. This might happen at any time of the night.

October

At the beginning of the month the earths were dug out, the summer's accumulation of debris was scattered and a mound of fresh earth appeared at the entrances. Vixens could now be seen emerging from their earths at about 5.30 pm. Much fox smell was associated with earths now in continuous use.

In 1964, there was a very interesting accumulation of field sign in the immediate vicinity of the breeding earth at Big Pit. During the month, sixty-five scats were collected from an area just around Big

Pit; some were found near the earths themselves but the majority were at field margins on well-marked trails around the hedges. This suggests a return by the fox population to what we have seen to be a characteristic winter habit of keeping to field margins, particularly when the area has been freshly ploughed.

Vocal activity has been noted during October at Kent's Green, and I recorded screams and fighting on 28 October 1966.

November

Frosts and wet weather are a great help in providing conditions suitable for the preservation of fox sign, particularly footprints. The rutting highways were now becoming established, although it was seldom that a scat was found on them. They were mostly still being deposited around the earths, though in 1965 the number decreased from sixty-five in October to twenty-eight in November. The earths themselves sometimes had scats by them but, again, field margins were the more favoured locations.

In 1965 vocal activity began in an area adjoining the one studied, namely on May Hill which rises to 981 ft OD. Barking was also heard in this month on the Cotswolds at Woodchester Park. In 1966, barking was commonly heard at Kent's Green—all single barks and yells.

No visual observations of the foxes were possible, mainly for lack of opportunity to make regular evening visits to the earths.

December

A great amount of field sign could again be detected, mainly in the form of footprint trails.

Scats were again found at field margins, but did not show the same concentration around the earths as in the previous two months. Any unusual objects in the environment were visited by the foxes and usually defecated upon. In 1964, a number of scats were collected from a large piece of rock salt which had been put out for cattle.

The earths showed signs of being inhabited and there were often fresh earth and footprints at their entrances. There was also a marked increase in the amount of fox scent both at the earths and on the trails.

Barking began at about 5 pm, which I also took to be the approximate emergence time, at least for vixens. Vocalisations of various kinds could be heard most frequently between 6 and 10 pm, with sporadic activity throughout much of the night. In this month daylight activity of the fox becomes quite common, particularly on the high ground of the Cotswolds.

From the evidence presented, it is perhaps reasonable to say that, for most of the year, fox activity is restricted to the hours of darkness, although when the days are longer the chances of seeing a fox in early morning or evening are quite high. There seems to be a difference in the activity pattern shown by males and females. Dog foxes are almost diurnal in January, and can also be seen during the day in December and February, whereas vixens at these times are strictly nocturnal, emerging from their earths just at nightfall. A further difference is that, during the winter months and probably for the rest of the year also, dog foxes are surface dwellers and are only occasionally beneath ground.

In late April and May, the vixen is the one to take to daytime activity of necessity, as she has hungry young cubs to feed. After June, there is a slackening off of daylight movement, which brings the foxes back to their normal crepuscular and nocturnal habits.

Fox
Senses

Many unproductive hours spent trying to watch foxes have made me realise why most of our knowledge of their habits is based on captive specimens and occasional chance observations. Even chance observations of the real fox are too often coloured by childhood impressions of the supposed character and ability of the fox and so tend to substantiate the generally accepted view that the fox is a cunning, scheming rogue of phenomenal resourcefulness when faced by danger or any difficulty in obtaining food.

How much, in reality, is this 'resourcefulness' an outward expression of the acute senses of the fox and its instinctive reaction to a given situation, rather than the product of a reasoning 'mind'?

HEARING

The large size of a fox's external ear or pinna suggests that sound plays a great part in its daily life. A fox uses its acute sense of hearing in the pursuit of small rodents, particularly field voles *Microtus agrestis* (Plate 6a). On a sunny afternoon in January 1965 I watched a fox 'voleing' on a grassy Cotswold hillside. It took up a position on a fallen log and looked interestedly at the grass around, which partly covered the log. Such habitats are ideal for voles, who make extensive surface runways amongst the grass stems and cannot easily be seen from above. Voles do, however, squeak as they scurry along their grass tunnels and the position of the fox's ears as it stood poised on the log suggested that it was listening intently. The large mobile ears were cupped forward and downwards, giving the animal a very alert expression. (See chapter heading.) It stood still for a few seconds and then, jack-knifing in a rapid, dive-like leap, brought both front paws down, presumably upon a vole. It then snapped its jaws down between the paws and a few seconds later resumed its walk. I very much doubt if it could have seen a vole beneath the excellent cover but it would have had no difficulty in hearing one.

As voles form an almost staple part of their diet, a fox's acute hearing power would seem to be a most important asset. A fox's attention must often be drawn by a sound to a supply of food, particularly to young birds with limited powers of flight. Injured and trapped animals may also draw attention to themselves, as did rabbits in the days of the gin trap, when the squeal of a trapped animal was only too commonly heard. Fortunately, many rabbits in this plight were quickly dispatched by badgers and foxes, who probably left only a few bits of fur, or a trapped limb, as evidence of the occurrence. After collecting such a free meal, a fox may also leave a dropping or urinate over the trap, which would popularly be taken to indicate the animal's contempt for man and his primitive methods of capturing prey. If, however, we remember that it is the fox's habit to leave his 'visiting card' on prey remains, then this behaviour at the trap needs no such sophisticated explanation.

Their sense of hearing also facilitates vocal communication between foxes over quite considerable distances and, like its close relative the dog, the fox is able to detect sound frequencies outside the range of the human ear.

Since the fox's survival in modern Britain is largely dependent upon its ability to remove itself from a source of potential danger as speedily as possible, early detection of any threat is vital to its existence. Here the ears are obviously of great advantage, if only because a fox can hear much better than we can. Even when there is no possibility of the fox having picked up human scent, one cracked twig or rustle of clothing will cause even a hunting fox to stop and look directly towards the source of the sound. If the animal receives no more danger signals, either audible or olfactory, it will probably trot away for a few yards, stop, look back with ears held forward to detect the slightest strange sound, turn again and only then, if confident, will it resume its activities. Usually, of course, the fox sees you before you see it, so that by the time you glimpse the retreating fox it will already have received a barrage of sound signals and been precipitated into a galloping retreat.

Although a fox has acute hearing and will react instantly on detecting a strange or danger-conveying sound I have, on three occasions, not exactly trodden on a fox, but have been within a yard or two of it before it has started up and made a hurried escape. Other observers have had even closer views of foxes but these were sleeping ones, said to have had their tails wrapped around their noses as they lay asleep in the open. A fox caught by hounds in this attitude is said to be 'chopped'.

How can these observations be explained? Lionel Edwards (1949) believes the reason for the chopping is due to the position of the fox's tail over its nose, whilst Brian Vesey-Fitzgerald (1965) thinks it is the very tired, probably recently hunted fox that is caught napping.

On the Cotswolds, near Stroud, a most interesting observation was made by Mr Trevor Walsh, who came upon a sleeping fox and, instead of making a hasty movement, did what every good field naturalist does—stayed quite still and watched the fox. It even occurred to him to measure the respiratory rate of the sleeping animal, which showed the extremely low number of twelve in five minutes! This observation was made on 29 February 1964 at 4 pm.

In support of Brian Vesey-Fitzgerald's suggestion that recently hunted foxes are sound sleepers is the fact that mental fatigue in humans can also cause deep sleep from which it is difficult to arouse them. Could this also be a possibility in the fox? Physical fatigue possibly but, under natural conditions (in which I include being hunted), I doubt whether a fox is subject to mental strain.

The most reasonable explanation of 'chopping' by hounds and of observations made of sleeping foxes is that it is a defensive attitude. Immobility and feigning death is a well established behaviour pattern amongst many animals, both invertebrates and vertebrates. Stick insects provide a good example amongst the lower animals whilst, among the mammals, the North American opossum is renowned for its 'stay put' attitude at the approach of danger. Ground-nesting birds bed low on their nests and hares crouch in a furrow to avoid detection. It is often only when a prey species moves or is scented that the predator becomes aware of its presence. Many other animals will adopt a passive attitude when faced with danger and so pass undetected by an enemy.

Considering the amount of folklore about the supposed intelligence of the fox, it is not surprising that, when a fox adopts this static method of escaping detection, it should be claimed as evidence of great cunning and skill. The fox is credited with extraordinary powers of reasoning and many people no doubt believe that a fox consciously sits down and thinks about ways and means of escaping from hounds or catching prey. Yet there are no more grounds for assuming this than that a stick insect thinks out its plan of action when danger threatens. The truth is that foxes, in common with many other animals, have various built-in devices to avoid enemies, one of which is to run away, and another to sham sleep or death. Both are stereotyped behaviour patterns and are not invoked by thought processes.

Young animals instinctively keep still when danger threatens and it is not surprising that most 'chopped' foxes seem to be cubs or juvenile animals. It is also probable that foxes adopt the static means of avoiding detection much more often than we realise, because we usually see only a running fox, not those lying still.

SMELL

Smell is probably the most vital single sense a fox possesses. It does not, I think, use its nose very much in hunting, for the type of animal normally eaten can be more easily detected by sight or sound, or the two combined. But smell is certainly of great help in detecting carrion and fruit, both of which are important food items for the fox.

I have yet to see a fox hunting with nose close to the trail, although they undoubtedly do so on occasion. One's normal impression of a foraging fox is of a very restless animal poking about in all directions, trotting a short distance and maybe leaping sideways occasionally as it picks up the sound of a small mammal or insect. I have never seen a fox carefully following a scent, allowing nothing to deter it from the trail, yet this was the way I once imagined a fox usually hunted.

The most important functions of a fox's nose are, in my opinion, the detection of enemies, particularly man, and for social information. A fox is not born with a built-in knowledge of the smells that denote an enemy; these have to be learned and upon the cub's ability quickly to make the necessary correlation often depends its fate. I recall an occasion in April 1964 when I visited Big Pit in search of scats. The paper bags I used for the collection made not a little noise, as did my own scrambling approach, so that I did not expect to see any cubs on the surface. Here I was wrong for, just as I was leaving, I looked up and saw three cubs interestedly watching me. They must have been nearly bowled over by the amount of human scent they received, yet neither smell, sight nor sound indicated danger to them. After I had watched them come and go around the mouth of the den, they slowly retired underground. Their emergence had presumably been prompted by the unusual happenings outside the earth and, once satisfied it was not food being brought by the vixen, they returned to their slumbers, having learned very little from the encounter.

Some days later I again visited the earth, this time for an evening watch, and installed myself in a tree with the wind, such as it was, blowing slightly across me but taking my scent well away from the earth. I expected to see cubs but hoped also to see the adult, and she it was that I saw. The buff-tipped vixen approached the far side of the pond from me, also up wind—ideal, I thought. As I watched, she stood on the bank above the earth and twice gave a low hiccup, shortly afterwards going right down to the earth to repeat the performance. Then, without looking round, she trotted away across the field. I sat in my tree until it was dark, but no cubs emerged. Had this been a danger signal to the cubs below ground? I suspected so but could not understand how the vixen knew there was danger, in the form of myself, near the earth. Not for a moment do I think that she was 'going into the teeth of danger' to warn her cubs, rather I suspect that during her approach to the earth she crossed my approach trail and that this set the danger signal for her. I am sure she did not detect my presence in the tree; if she had her retreat would have been instant and rapid.

A further encounter with a vixen with cubs took place at Clewes' Pond Earth in May 1966. I was watching the vixen play with her cubs at some little distance from the earth, which was between them and where I was standing. The vixen brought the cubs back towards the earth at a gallop but just before she reached where I was standing near a gate in the evening gloom, she picked up my scent and gave a low growl that sent the cubs into the hedge adjacent to my gate. Then, hiccupping fairly quietly, she walked slowly in a half circle around me, all the while looking towards me but not, I think, being able to pick out my form. Having completed the half circle, she stopped hiccupping and quietly made off towards the local farm, silhouetted in the light from one of its windows (Fig 7). The cubs were noticeably more difficult to watch after this encounter, evidence that the warning growl and hiccup given by the vixen, associated as it must have been with my scent, had taught the young cubs a vital lesson. They now began automatically to make the necessary correlation for a fox— human scent and danger—and my observations were the poorer for it, although I'm sure some young foxes learn less quickly than others.

An animal does not, of course, use each sense separately but rather co-ordinates the information it receives from all. Scent, in particular is, however, used to locate buried animals, as I know to my cost in my own garden. All too often for the health of the local badger population, I have brought to me bodies of badgers killed on the local roads, and by measuring and weighing the bodies and analysing the stomach contents I have been able to discover much useful information about the badger's feeding habits.

My garden is, therefore, the resting place for a number of badgers and foxes and, no matter how deeply I bury the bodies, they are almost invariably dug up during the winter by local foxes who leave their characteristic droppings and footprints near the scene. Similar activities take place in my neighbour's garden when dead hens from the battery are buried. The fox must locate this buried food by scent, just as it rediscovers food caches it has made for itself.

EYESIGHT

It is very difficult indeed to make a pronouncement on foxes' visual ability; there are many different opinions and little that one can do to test any of them in the field. All I can do is to draw such conclusions as I can from my own observations.

In June 1966, I was walking towards Three Oaks Pit from Big Pit at about 8 pm. These two pits are dug into one side of a small hill and as I was traversing the edge of the cornfield that covered it, part of the field was hidden on the other side of the rise. Unknown to me,

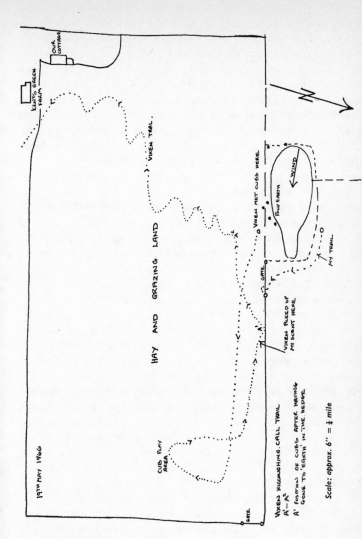

7. Fieldbook drawing of the trail taken by the hiccupping vixen after our encounter near her earth

a fox was taking an almost parallel course to mine on the other side of the hill, walking among corn which was about a foot high. As I came round my side of the hill I saw the fox and stood stock-still. The fox had not seen me and continued walking, carrying a blackbird in its mouth. Then quite suddenly, when past me, it turned its head, saw me and galloped off towards the hedge. All unknowingly, it was heading towards a farmer who had come to inspect his bullocks in the adjoining field and it must have noticed this second human threat as it went through the hedge for it veered right, crossed the corner of the bullocks' field and shot out through the other hedge into an adjoining pasture. Once clear of the second hedge the fox stopped, looked back at the bullocks' field and then, with a marked slackening of pace, resumed its normal trotting gait, occasionally making slight detours to investigate isolated clumps of coarse grass.

Two things are, I think, important here. I said the fox saw me—but did it see a human outline and react to this, or was I just an unusual shape in an otherwise familiar setting? If we say the former, we are then crediting the fox with ability to abstract from its surroundings the shape 'man' and to carry in its brain this 'picture' which enables it to recognise the shape 'man' on subsequent occasions. Does a fox see in this essentially human way? I think not; more likely it only records a change in its surroundings which, in itself, can produce fear and an escape reaction. We have been considering a stationary human being; a moving one is certainly seen but probably only because it is moving.

I suggest that the bird-carrying fox reacted to me only because I was an unusual object in a familiar place. In the previous chapter on watching foxes, I mentioned that I always get to know my surroundings before beginning a dusk watch and have often only been aware of the presence of a fox by noting a shape where previously there has been nothing. It is in this way, I think, that a fox 'sees' a stationary human being, or any other animal for that matter.

The second interesting feature of this incident is how quickly the disturbed fox resumed normal activities although it was still only about 100 yards away from the source of its disturbance. This was also a feature of the incident with the hiccupping vixen and the cubs. The vixen, too, returned to her normal activities very soon after what must have been a severe shock.

A hunted fox is said sometimes to kill for food whilst being hunted, and this is taken as showing the fox's contempt for the pursuing hounds. But is it not what we would expect a fox to do—return to its normal routine as soon as possible? Once there is a fair distance between it and the hounds, the immediate stimulus to run is reduced and replaced by normal activities, including killing other animals for food. This may not make such an interesting story but, to me at least, it makes much more sense, and fits in very well with my observations on unhunted foxes.

The fox has quite large eyes and the amount of light allowed to fall on the light-sensitive layers at the back of the eyes is determined by the size of the aperture, that is of the pupil. The shape and size of the pupil are, in turn, determined by the iris which acts as a diaphragm. To protect the delicate, light-sensitive layer or retina from being damaged by excessive light, the size of the pupil is reduced by the action of muscles in the iris, reducing the pupil to a small circle in man but to a narrow vertical slit in the cat and fox (Plate 6b). Conversely, when light intensity is reduced, so the size of the pupil increases to let as much light as possible into the eye. The ability of an animal to see in poor light is thus largely dependent upon the structure of the retina; animals that are usually active in darkness often have good night vision.

How good a fox's night vision is, I do not know, but it is probably as good as a cat's and certainly much better than a man's. My only direct indication of a fox's night vision was obtained during an evening watch in an orchard one August. I knew that the fox usually appeared in this particular place about 9.30 pm, so a little before this time I found a convenient tree to lean against and waited with binoculars ready. Darkness soon made unaided visual observation impossible, and I began to scan between the trees with my binoculars. After about a quarter of an hour, my arms and eyes rebelled and I was just about to leave when I decided to make one more pan with the glasses. I normally raise my binoculars to my eyes very slowly but on this occasion I was so convinced there was no fox in the orchard that I picked them up quickly and was just in time to see a fox retreating from me at a gallop. It must have been about fifty yards from me when I made the fatal quick movement, yet it detected it even at that distance and in very poor light, whereas I could not see the fox with my naked eye. So there, at least, is a little bit of field evidence to support the supposition that the fox has good night vision and further confirmation of my belief that movement is the determining factor in whether or not a fox sees an object.

There is yet another sense which involves the use of all the sense organs mentioned, as well as the general body surface. This is called the kinaesthetic sense, and is developed by an animal's constant use of a particular area as a result of which it gets to know 'the feel' of the environment. Vibrissae, or whiskers, are aids to sensory perception in most mammals. In foxes, these are thick, black hairs and their position is shown on the drawing of a dead vixen in Fig 8. Vibrissae are extra sense organs, particularly useful in giving the animal information about the size of opening through which it can pass without fear of being trapped. They also give information about the general proximity of objects in the animal's environment—a useful aid in the dark.

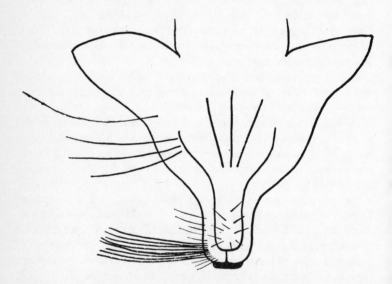

8. Vibrissae or whiskers, drawn from a dead fox

All the senses, plus vibrissae, provide information about the animal's surroundings, so that it can move about even in complete darkness without falling over or bumping into objects. We make use of this ability when we cross a familiar room, in darkness, to turn on the light. We know what furniture is where and, subconsciously, how many steps to take before we reach out our hand at the correct level to find the switch.

Complete familiarity with surroundings is particularly important to small mammals, such as shrews, which seem to have poorly developed eyesight but are nevertheless able to negotiate very rapidly their own runway systems. They do this so automatically that, should an obstacle over which the shrew normally jumps be removed, the animal will still jump when it arrives at the former position of the obstacle. It is not suggested that a fox would behave in a similar manner but it probably has just as much knowledge of its home area as the shrew, though it differs from the latter in that a change in surroundings is detected at once and, if not obviously dangerous, quickly investigated and probably urinated or defecated upon.

A fox in its home area has built up, as a result of its well-developed sense organs, a very detailed knowledge of its surroundings. Not only does it have a visual, but also a smell and sound picture of its environment. Recognising this, we can understand why it is so very difficult to watch foxes for more than a few minutes. Not only are they usually on the move but, if one tries to follow them, one is bound to make a slight change in the environment which will be detected by the fox. It need be only a slight movement of the hand, a small bird disturbed from the hedge or a stray current of air, anything which brings to the fox a very slight human scent. Even a glimpse of a stationary human, as we have seen, will cause flight.

There is, therefore, no need to invoke extreme intelligence on behalf of the fox to explain why it is such an elusive animal; it is so, simply because it has such superbly developed senses.

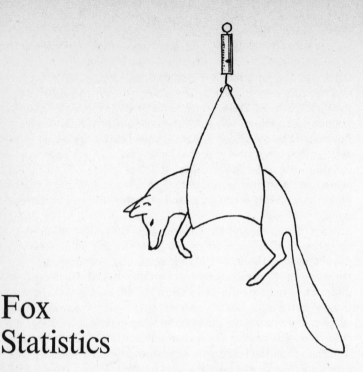

Fox
Statistics

The red foxes of Europe and India, as well as those of North America, where they were probably introduced in the eighteenth century, are all members of the genus *Vulpes*. There are a number of species of *Vulpes* which show slight but, it is believed, distinctive differences from one another in some physical characteristics. The European red fox is *Vulpes vulpes* (Linnaeus, 1758), the North American—*V. regalis* or *V. fulva* and so on. Even then, taxonomists have found it necessary to make finer distinctions between, for example, foxes from northern and central Europe, each of which is given a sub-specific name, although the characters that separate them are very slight and require a close study of skeletal remains in order to classify them.

According to Miller, the fox in Europe can be divided into a number of subspecies. A northern form, *Vulpes vulpes vulpes* (Linnaeus, 1758), was thought to be confined to the Scandinavian peninsula and to be the largest type of fox, having a large skull and heavy body with only slight gaps between the premolar teeth. A second or central European fox, which includes the British fox *V.v. crucigera* (Bechstein, 1789), is said to be smaller than the northern form and to have rather widely-spaced premolars which are seldom, if ever, in contact. A third subspecies, *V.v. silacea* (Miller, 1907) from the Iberian peninsula, is said to be smaller still, to be slightly lighter in colour than the other two subspecies, and to have smaller teeth with widely-spaced premolars.

It used to be a characteristic of taxonomists that they split species into many subspecies, based on very minute differences detected when studying dead specimens. There has since been a change in emphasis in biology and animals are now considered much more in terms of populations than as isolated individuals. We also now recognise that a species can show a great amount of variation, particularly when it occurs over a large geographical area, without it being necessary, or even desirable, to split it into subspecies. In other words, we have passed from being 'splitters' to 'lumpers'. The result is that the status of some of these old subspecies is being questioned and we now usually give only two names, the generic and specific, to an animal. There has to be a very good reason before a third is added.

Miller (1912) only recognised *V.v. crucigera* in Britain but, more recently, some authors have claimed that the Scottish fox (which may have been imported) belongs to the subspecies *V.v. vulpes* of Scandinavia.

The skulls of the Scottish dog foxes examined by Hattingh were significantly larger than those of English dog foxes. Together with Tetley (1941) and Mathews (1951), he claims that there is no distinction between the Scottish and Scandinavian fox, concluding that both are the large *V. vulpes vulpes* subspecies.

Hattingh (1956) compared the weights of the Scottish fox with those from England and found that the former were larger, that is heavier, than the average English fox but that the differences were not significant.

Average weight of English fox:	Male	14·716 ±	0·249 lb
	Female	11·8 ±	0·249 lb
Average weight of Scottish fox:	Male	14·816 ±	1·37 lb
	Female	12·6 ±	0·91 lb

(Data from Hattingh)

If we now compare the average weight of the Norwegian (i.e. Scandinavian) fox with that of the Scottish fox, we find the latter considerably heavier and not similar as might have been expected. The male Norwegian fox, with an average weight of 5·9 kg (approximately 13 lb) is only slightly heavier than the female Scottish fox at 12·6 lb. The average weights and maximum recorded weights of foxes from different countries are given in Appendix C.

If, however, a comparison is made between the skull measurements given by Miller for *V.v.v. vulpes* and similar measurements for foxes from England, Scotland and Russia we find that the Scottish fox skull is not similar to, but larger than the Scandinavian, though the tooth size and jaw dimensions are fairly similar. It appears to me that *V.v. vulpes L.* has the jaws and teeth of the Scottish and the cranial measurements of the English fox, which Miller distinguishes as *V.v. crucigera*. This comparison of both body weights and skull measurements as published would, therefore, seem to suggest that the Scottish fox is distinguishable from the Scandinavian, contrary to the view previously held.

Miller does give another character which he used to distinguish between the two subspecies, the well-developed secondary cusp on the premolars of the *vulpes* subspecies. These are found also on the *crucigera* subspecies and Miller said that different geographical regions have foxes with different sized cusps. One wonders how good a systematic character cusp size is in this case.

One point was finally cleared up by Hattingh who found that there was no difference between the Westmorland so-called 'hill fox' and that found in the lowland area, whereas it had previously been thought that the hill fox was the larger.

If we remember that the only differences between the subspecies are slight variations in size of body and skull and in the spacing of the premolars, we realise that this subspecies question need not be of much concern to the field naturalist. One even doubts how valuable are the characters upon which the different subspecies are based, particularly when one compares the available measurements. There is a generalisation called Bergman's rule which states that animals tend to be larger in the northern and smaller in the southern part of their range. May not this be applied to the foxes we have considered, and is not it to be expected that foxes in Scotland should be larger than those in England, and Russian foxes larger than Spanish, when considered as a population rather than as isolated individuals?

It may well be that the foxes from all the countries mentioned and others besides, do not need to be split into subspecies as their weight and size in each country will, in any event, be largely determined by food supply. As for teeth size, one would expect foxes in the north of the range to be larger than those from the south. A poorly-fed, large-boned animal will, however, probably not be as heavy as a well-fed smaller one.

A leading Russian authority, Ognev (1931), claims that tooth size and premolar gap are both very variable characteristics and that Miller's data does not support his assertion that *V.v. vulpes* is larger than *V.v. crucigera*. One feels, therefore, that a thorough review of the classification of the fox is needed.

Physical Characteristics of the Red Fox

There is little need to describe what a fox looks like, for it is one of the few wild British mammals that really cannot be misidentified. There are, however, certain points that may not be well known and so deserve comment.

Colour

The colour of mammals is determined by the distribution of pigmented hairs over the body. Coloured hairs are disposed in patterns that are usually characteristic for the species in broad outline, but some species often show considerable individual variation in the shade and distribution of the variously coloured hairs.

My own observations on both living and dead foxes indicate that each fox differs, usually slightly, in some aspect of its coloration. Some are reddish brown, others decidedly ginger, whilst grey foxes are fairly commonly seen. Some foxes have white chests and underparts, others have these areas sooty or nearly black. The tip of the tail, or tag, shows a wide colour variation and may be black, white or, as in the case of one of the Kent's Green vixens, decidedly yellow/buff. A white tail tag does not indicate a dog fox, as used to be thought, and we know that only a proportion of foxes have the white or albino tip, which is not, therefore, a characteristic of the species as some authors suggest. From the little information we have on this subject (Corbet, 1963), roughly 73 per cent of fifteen foxes examined from England and Wales and just over 87 per cent of thirty-one Scottish foxes had the white tag. The conclusion must be that the majority of British foxes do have a white tail tip but that this feature is not the monopoly of the male.

Cubs of the same litter that I have watched have shown individual colour variation, some being greyer or darker red than their fellows, some showing white tail tags, others red or black, even when only five or six weeks old. I have not examined new-born fox cubs but Ognev claims that they have brownish-black, short hair on the trunk and abdomen, rather greyer paws and head, a band of rusty-grey hairs across the forehead and a small patch of pure white on the chest. The tail, this author says, is covered with blackish-brown, short hair with a pure white tip which, he claims, is highly character-istic. Douglas (1966) also refers to the white tail tip he observed on Scottish fox cubs. Other authors describe the cub coat as being chocolate brown.

Whatever the original cub-coat colour, it rapidly changes after the cubs begin to emerge from the earths at about four weeks, and they gradually assume the colour of the adult. The change from cub coat to adult presumably takes place without a moult and certainly I have found little field sign to indicate a moult at this time, although a few stray hairs are found in cub droppings collected near dens in April and May.

It would appear that just as no two sets of human finger-prints are identical, so no two fox skins are alike, at least when examined in detail. Having said that, I will now generalise and indicate the most frequently seen distribution of colour in a fox pelt:

Lower side of face, chin, throat, chest and belly—whitish.
Eye stripe, backs of ears, lower front parts of both fore and hind legs and paws—black.
Distinctive tail tag—white, black or dark red.
Hip region and buttocks—often tinged with grey.
General body colour—reddish brown.

There are occasional references in the available literature to foxes whose colour differs markedly from the typical one just described. In Finland, of 2,864 skins examined, 99 per cent were of the red type, 0·6 per cent were said to be black-bellied, 0·3 per cent were cross foxes and 0·1 per cent black (Oksala, 1954). No comparable data are available in this country but we do have references, particu-larly in hunting literature, to foxes that probably fit into one or other of these categories.

Black-bellied

These foxes have dark reddish-coloured backs but instead of the typical white chest and off-white belly theirs are dark grey to black. Frances Pitt mentions a fox killed in Shropshire which had a sooty throat and stomach, and a light rusty yellow back. She records that a local taxidermist found about one in forty of the foxes he received to treat were of this type and seemed to come particularly from Wales. Lionel Edwards describes a Hampshire fox with a black head, belly and brush, but a back of normal colour. Brian Vesey-Fitzgerald records four examples of foxes with smoke-blue chests and these, I think, also probably belong in this category. In February 1966, a vixen was killed by a car in a lane near Newent, Glos, and whilst skinning the body I noticed that she had a dark belly and chest, the latter having a small spot of white. This is the only example of black-bellied foxes I have examined. In the USSR it is said that the black-bellied form is more typical of mountainous than low ground.

Cross Foxes

Most foxes have a band of slightly darker pigmented hair running across the back between the shoulders and extending down the back of the animal towards the tail, so producing the typical cross. The cross fox has this band particularly well developed, the hairs being very dark. The general body colour is also darker than in the normal red fox. This type does not seem to have been recorded in this country, although it no doubt occurs.

Albino Foxes

A total lack of any body pigment produces an animal which has white or yellowish-white fur and pink eyes. The eye colour is produced because the usual eye pigment is absent and the blood capillaries at the back of the eye do not have their pink-blood colour masked. Albinism is a genetically determined recessive feature which can, therefore, be transmitted to later generations. In fact, it rarely shows up in a wild community of animals and when it does, its adaptive disadvantage means that the albino animal seldom lives to breed.

There are records of white, presumably albino, foxes from Dartmoor, and at least five records of them from Whaddon Chase.

Grey Foxes

All the adult foxes I have examined have had a certain amount of grey hair on their flanks. This is not usually obvious when watching foxes in the field, although my buff-tipped vixen did have two very prominent grey patches on her haunches which were clearly visible during my daytime observations of her in May and June 1966. The large fox that lived near Clewes' Farm Earth during the winter of 1965–6 was a very grey specimen and, I think, the one I have called, on vocal evidence, the 'wo-wo' fox.

Harrison Mathews (1952) discusses the grey fox question and the claim that there are in Scotland two distinct colour forms or phases. One is said to be large and pale, weighing seventeen to nineteen pounds and having basically red fur with dark, but not black, legs and feet as in typical *V.v. crucigera*. The other is smaller and predominantly grey but also has some dark chestnut hair and weighs twelve to fifteen pounds.

About the only method of ageing a fox, albeit roughly, is to examine the amount of wear shown by the teeth. A great amount is presumed to indicate a mature, probably old animal, whilst little wear would be expected in the teeth of young animals. The teeth of Scottish grey foxes were examined and showed that the animals were all fully adult vixens, some probably quite old, and Mathews suggests that greyness is possibly associated with age and small size with sex. Grey foxes have been seen in both highland and lowland regions of the British Isles but are probably more common locally on high ground. We do not know for sure if the grey animal is a colour phase or, as suggested, a characteristic of old foxes, mainly vixens.

TABLE 1: Fox. Age determination based on the amount of tooth wear

	No. of males	Per cent Mature	Per cent Mature old	No. of females	Per cent Mature	Per cent Mature old
E. Europe and Russia (U.S.S.R.) (from Ognev)	81	35	12	51	53	35
W. Europe (Miller)	33	54·5	15	12	66	33

On the basis of information published on foxes for various parts of the world, I have calculated the percentage of mature animals of each sex killed, presumably without sex selection, over a limited period of time. It appears that the chances of the dog fox reaching maturity are less than those of the vixen and he stands even less chance of reaching old age.

The correlation between the percentage of old animals of each sex in the two sets of figures is probably more than coincidence. It suggests that if, as Harrison Mathews thinks, greyness is associated with age, we should find more grey vixens than dog foxes, and this is well borne out by the Scottish evidence. Unless there is a close link between greyness and females, one would expect to find grey males occasionally, as I think I have at Clewes' Farm Earth.

Silver and Blue Foxes

In Europe, owing to the escape of imported North American silver foxes from fox farms, there are other colour phases of the fox now living and breeding in the wild including, in Scandinavia, silver and blue types. The former is basically a black animal in which prominent white tips to the long guard hairs give a silvery appearance to the pelt. There seem to be various types of blue foxes, including one called a cross blue, which has a prominent, almost black, cross-shaped pattern of hairs across the shoulders and running down the back.

Russian authors mention blue and silver foxes as being present in the northern parts of the red foxes' range, so not all the blue foxes in northern Europe need necessarily be descended from the feral North American form.

Samson Fox

This woolly-haired variety is characterised by an almost complete lack of guard hairs. It is occasionally found on fox farms, and is also present in the wild-fox population in Finland and North America. This so-called Samson fox (Oksala, 1954), has been recognised since the 1930s and seems to have been particularly numerous in the mid 1940s, when there was a low local fox population.

The 'guard-hairless' character seems to be inheritable and is thought to be recessive to normal-type hair. The Samson fox is also said to differ from the normal in claw structure, metabolic rate and behaviour. They seem to eat larger quantities of refuse than do the normal foxes, but the same amount of game animals.

I have found one other reference to a fox lacking guard hairs

(Troitskaya, 1958). This was a very heavily parasitised male cub less than ten months old. It was host to five species of parasitic worm, no fewer than 1,634 individual worms being present. Not surprisingly, the nutritional state of this cub (from Northern Asia) was said to be poor. I know of no records of Samson foxes in this country.

Black or Blackish-Brown Foxes

Black, or so-called melanistic forms of red foxes are found over much of the animal's range and are reported from North America, Alaska, Siberia, Russia and Europe.

There are also black foxes in the British Isles. Brian Vesey-Fitzgerald records one killed by the Belvoir Hunt in the 1850s, also others unsuccessfully hunted by the Meynell just after the Second World War. Another, it seems, was shot near Rowledge, Surrey, in 1960 and Mivarnt mentions a blackish-brown fox as being found in Wales. The relative paucity of records suggests that black foxes may be as scarce in this country as they seem to be throughout the foxes' range.

There appear to be two distinct types of black or so-called blackish-brown foxes in the northern hemisphere. Although having a similar outward appearance, or phenotype, they seem to have a different internal genetic composition or genotype. They are distinguished as the Canadian and Alaskan black fox, the latter being also found in Siberia, Russia and Fenno-Scandia, while the former is confined as a native animal at least to the North American continent.

Some evidence to support Ognev's claim that dark foxes are more frequently found in more northern locations is provided by figures given by Voipio (1950), who found that there were slightly more black and black-bellied cross foxes in the northern province of Finland than in the country as a whole. Even then only one black, six cross and four black-bellied forms were found among a total of 588 foxes examined. In Finland as a whole, there were two black, ten cross and seventeen black-bellied phases out of a total of 2,864 skins.

It seems probable that the colour of foxes in any one area is partly, at least, dependent upon geographical situation. Certain colour phases seem to be associated with a particular habitat, although by no means confined to it. There will, of course, be a certain amount of individual variation from the dominant colour phase in any one habitat, and where the latter are poorly demarcated there should be considerable overlap of colour phases. One might, therefore, expect

74

the greatest colour range among foxes at the junction of two well-defined habitats.

The various colour phases of *Vulpes vulpes* are:

(1) Red fox:

    A: Red with white belly: common fox colour and seems to be the most common type at least in Europe.

    B: Red with black belly: more likely to be found in mountains. This seems to conform to the observation mentioned by Frances Pitt that black-bellied forms came mostly from Wales.

    C: Light yellow: sea types, tundra foxes.

    D: Flame: Brightly-coloured, golden red, said to be sometimes found in mountains but less commonly than black-bellied, also occur in Scandinavia—the so-called 'Norwegian fox'.

    E: Cross fox or cross-patterned: more characteristic of forest, together with other dark phases.

(2) Blue foxes:

    F: Simple blue: more common in forest belts in European part of USSR and Siberia, where it is said to be the dominant form. In other northern areas in Russia, approximately one in ten is blue.

    G: Silver fox: white-tipped guard hairs giving silvery effect to the pelt.

    H: Cross: a top-quality blue fox with a black shoulder cross.

(3) Black foxes:

    I: The black or blackish-brown fox: said to be as rare in Russia as it appears to be in other parts of Europe. Slightly more abundant at edge of tundra where red form is scarce.

Generally there is a tendency for mountain and forest foxes to be more vividly coloured than lowland forms. It is also possible that grey foxes are more characteristic of mountains than lowland although this may, as we have seen, be due to age of the fox. There is some evidence to support the view that upland foxes are larger than lowland forms, but this again may be due to age factors, although the skull and teeth of the Scottish fox (not the Westmorland) are larger than their English cousins from the lowlands.

To generalise again, the further south one goes in the range of *Vulpes vulpes*, the smaller and lighter in colour the foxes seem to become, with desert and steppe foxes having particularly pale pelts. Again, hair is longer, silkier, more dense and strongly pigmented in the northern foxes, and it has been noticed that even domesticated silver foxes do not produce such dense pelts in this country as they do in their native North America.

In the British Isles, as we have seen, there are representatives of a number of the different colour phases mentioned. There are definite rare records of black and black-bellied foxes, with a number of variations on the red fox colour scheme. While we have no records of the cross fox, I think it extremely likely that it does occur but it has not, to my knowledge, yet been described.

It is highly unlikely that the British fox will show the variations in colour and size that can be seen over a greater geographical range and in countries, such as on the Continent, with more varied elevations. There is also the complicating factor of a large number of foxes having been imported into this country from various parts of the Continent, particularly in the eighteenth and nineteenth centuries, to increase our native population for hunting purposes. Lacking, as we now do, really large areas of well-defined varied habitats, it is only to be expected that the British fox—and the English one in particular—should show a wide range of coat colours quite unrelated to any physical or geographical factor.

All the fox phases discussed above can be considered to be merely varieties of *Vulpes vulpes*, although many subspecies have often been named on the basis of pelt colour, size of skull and body. There seems to be little value in separating subspecies on such highly variable characteristics, particularly when they seem to be at least partly dependent on geographical position, each type forming part of a graded series either from north to south or from high ground to low.

Moulting

In this process the whole of the fox's coat is shed and replaced by new hair. The timing of the moult is reasonably constant, depending upon latitude, and the fox only undergoes this process once a year, beginning in late spring and ending in the early autumn. The moult takes between two and three months to complete, depending upon the individual.

It has been shown experimentally (Bassett & Llewellyn, 1947), with silver foxes in captivity, that if the animals are subjected to an increased amount of daily illumination before the moult in April, the time taken for its completion is reduced though it does not start any earlier. This means that the silver fox fur becomes prime, or of greatest commercial value, about a month earlier than with similar foxes which have not been subject to the increased illumination.

The hair is not shed from all regions of the body at the same time in the silver fox; it normally begins on the feet and face and spreads along the back, the tail being the last area to lose the old hair.

The two main types of hair in a fox's pelt, as in many other mammals, are the guard hairs and underfur. The guard hairs not only give physical protection but are also mainly responsible for giving the animal its typical colour. These long guard hairs are relatively sparse by comparison with the soft underfur comprising the second hair type. This forms a dense woolly layer which traps a great deal of air to give good thermal insulation and prevent any rapid heat loss from the body surface. The typical grey underfur is very much thicker in winter than in summer, causing the guard hairs to stand up almost at right angles to the skin surface and so giving the fox a much heavier outline than his sleek summer appearance when the guard hairs are lying almost parallel to the skin.

During the summer, fox scats often contain a few fox hairs swallowed accidentally during grooming operations. Scott (1943) reports finding, and gives a photograph of wads of fox hair with two small holes in them. He measured the distance between them and decided they were left by the fox's canine teeth as it used them to comb loose hair from its coat. I have not found this field sign at Kent's Green and one would no doubt need considerable luck to do so.

Cubs gradually get the adult coat during the spring as the guard hairs grow up and cover the original, woolly, underfur-like coat, and they do not undergo a moult until the following spring. The adult coat colour seems to be slightly lighter in the summer.

Size of the British Fox

The weight of an animal is usually taken to be an indication of its size. In England, the average weight of forty dog foxes examined by Hattingh was $14\cdot7 \pm 0\cdot213$ lb ($6\cdot7$ kg), and of thirty-four vixens, $11\cdot8 \pm 0\cdot249$ lb ($5\cdot4$ kg).

For Scotland, the average weights of five dog foxes was $14\cdot8 \pm$

1·37 lb (8·7 kg); and of five vixens, 12·6 ± 0·91 kg, both slightly heavier than for the English fox.

There are, of course, records of individuals whose weight far exceeds these averages. Millais (1904) records one weighing 10·4 kg. A Cumberland male fox weighed 23 lb 10 oz, whilst there are a number of 20-lb records, usually males.

For Kent's Green I obtained the following records:

Sex	Killed	Weight
Vixen	Dec 1965	14 lb
Dog	Dec 1965	13·5 lb. This was a bob-tailed fox
Dog	Dec 1964	16 lb

When average weights are considered, it is clear that vixens tend to be lighter and are therefore said to be smaller than dog foxes. In fact, there is considerable individual variation, some vixens being extremely heavy and some dogs relatively light.

Cub Weights

At birth, fox cubs weigh about 100 gm but there can be considerable weight differences between members of the same litter; one litter ranged from 85 gm for the smallest to 150 gm for the heaviest (Lund, 1959). It is dangerous to compare the weights of a number of litters from the same area, because there are often considerable differences in age between neighbouring litters. (Male cubs tend to be heavier at birth than females of the same litter.)

The cubs soon increase in weight, being about 1,130 gm at six weeks, 3,160 gm at four and a half months, and continuing to increase until mid-winter, when they become sexually mature and breed. This is slightly later than for mature foxes not in their first season.

Length

The length of the animal as measured from the tip of the snout to the tip of the last vertebra of the tail will, of course, depend partly on age and sex, and may also be influenced by nutritional factors, all of which affect the overall genetically determined potential length of the individual fox.

Length of tail also varies greatly, even in foxes with the same body length. Three male foxes measured by Hattingh, all with a body length of 65·5 cm, had brushes of 38, 40 and 42·5 cm respectively, while one of 65 cm body length had a tail of 43·5 cm. The longest brush he measured in dog foxes was 47 cm. The vixens, with a shorter body than that of the dog, seem to have a proportionately shorter tail, the longest from Hattingh's figures being 42 cm. As with dog foxes, vixens of the same body size have varied tail lengths. Five with a body length of 63 cm had tails of 36·5, 38, 39, 40·5 and 41 cm, respectively.

An average adult fox has a head and body length of 65 cm, or nearly twenty-six inches, with the brush adding another sixteen inches (40 cm) giving an overall length from snout to tip of tail, excluding end hairs, of 105 cm (3 ft 6 in). There are, of course, records of giant foxes—two males—4 ft 5 in and 4 ft 6 in in length, but these are rare.

The hairs at the tip of the brush, projecting beyond the last tail vertebra, vary considerably in length. They are longest in the dog fox, averaging 87 mm with a range from 30 to 125 mm and, in the vixen, averaging 83 mm with range of 25 to 120 mm. (Figures from Lund.) Average lengths and ranges are given in Appendix F, which includes information from Continental sources.

Sexual Differences in Foxes

The fact that the vixen is, on average, lighter in weight than the dog fox is of little value to the man in the field trying to distinguish between the sexes. I know of no easy way of doing so and am not alone in my ignorance, for no authors appear ever to have committed themselves to defining precisely how to distinguish male from female fox when observing them at a distance. Some suggestions are given by Talbot, who claims that the position of the head during cantering, the fineness of the neck and the way the brushes are carried can be used as aids to sexing. I have not noticed anything significantly different in the way the two sexes hold their heads or tails, but as I am not certain that any of the foxes I have watched have been dogs I am not really competent to assess the validity of Talbot's claims. Talbot also mentions one difference between the sexes that can, I think, be detected if one has a good head-on view of the fox—not the most usual view, in my experience! Certainly, it has been useful to me in indicating the female status of foxes I have watched emerging from their earths when I have been using a torch. The difference concerns the width and 'domeing' of the forehead between the ears. I first noticed that the dog fox was much wider and more rounded in this region than the vixen when I compared the bodies of a dog

F   79

fox and a vixen killed on the roads. I cannot do better than repeat, as Talbot says, that the ears and snout form a V shape in the vixen and a W shape in the dog when viewed head-on. Figure 9 will, perhaps, help to explain the observed difference.

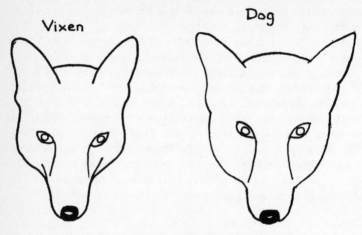

9. Front views of vixen and dog fox

The W of the dog fox is particularly well shown in those which have a dark inverted V pattern of hair running from its apex above and between the eyes, crossing the face and running through the inner angle of the eyes, ending on either side of the snout.

Having hinted that W and V patterns by themselves are not infallible methods of sexing your fox in the field, I might well be asked how I was able so confidently to identify the buff-tipped vixen mentioned earlier. In that instance, conclusive evidence was provided when I saw her briefly suckling a cub one morning in April 1966; I had also watched her squat to urinate—an action seldom seen in dog foxes. The only other and sure method of sexing is to witness copulation in foxes, but as this probably takes place at night, it is easier said than done. Failing these guides, to sex your foxes in the field you must either capture or destroy them, or spend literally weeks of watching in the hope of detecting, as I did with the buff-tipped vixen, features of their habits that will give the required information. Unfortunately, the often heard story that a white tail tag indicates a dog fox and absence of it a vixen, is not supported by fact.

Sexing captive foxes is an altogether different matter and Hurrell (1962) claims that the dog can be recognised as having a wider snout than the vixen.

Weight Fluctuations in the Fox (Graph in Appendix E)

Even the small amount of work done on the weight of foxes killed at different times of the year shows that quite large seasonal variations take place, the average fox weight varying from 12·2 lb to approximately 14 lb between February and May in England.

Hattingh found that English dog foxes lose, on average, 1·3 lb in the hundred days between February and May. A similar but smaller loss, only half that of our foxes, occurs in Norway (Lund, 1959). Loss in weight in spring is not, it seems, confined to wild foxes, as captive silver foxes are at their heaviest in mid-winter and then begin to lose weight until February or March.

Norwegian vixens show considerable monthly weight variations with lows in mid-winter and early summer, and peaks in between. Hattingh also found that the weights of English vixens varied rather irregularly but generally rose from a low in February to a high level in March and April, after which there was a drop in May. This fluctuation is similar to that found in Norwegian vixens.

In the light of field observations, what reasons can be given for these seasonal variations in both sexes of foxes? We must remember that, due to the difference in latitude between Norway and England, there will probably be a difference of about a month in the date of the various events in a fox's life cycle. This would mean that events taking place in May in Norway, would, on average, take place in April in England, due to the later date of the rut in more northern regions.

The winter low in the vixen's weight occurs at the time of the rut, when the dog fox weight also seems to decrease. As the dog foxes are very active, both day and night, at this time of year and tend to wander widely, one might expect a slight weight loss. If, as I have done on many occasions, one follows a fox trail in January, very little evidence will be seen of foxes having looked for or caught prey. Most of the trails are unbroken by detours, as they are at other times of the year, and I get the impression of great activity but little effort to obtain food. The vixens which, in January, are, I believe, much more confined to their earths during daylight hours, are probably physically impeded from food gathering by the attendant dog foxes, and certainly the barking which takes place in winter would warn a potential prey animal of the predator's approach. I think, therefore, that the mid-winter loss in weight is due to the effects of the rut and the general restlessness of the animals at this time of year; also that the foxes live off the ample reserves of fat they store up under the skin and around the intestines during the preceding late autumn.

After mating has taken place in January, one would expect the weight of the vixens to increase as the pregnancy progresses. This rise will end abruptly at parturition or birth which, in this country at least, usually takes place in February or March. After this, the vixen suckles the cubs and is usually, I believe, solely responsible for the daytime feeding of the cubs when they start to be weaned; she is also probably unaided at night. This pressure of nutrition is possibly the reason for the low average weight of vixens in June in Norway and May in England. May, it will be remembered, is the month during which I have made many daylight observations on vixens which were very active in feeding their cubs. Once the latter begin partly to feed themselves (from about six weeks), and when daytime visits to the cubs by the vixen are no longer necessary—as in late May at Kent's Green—then the body weight of the vixens can, theoretically, begin to increase again. This is also what actually happens in practice and the rise continues until they reach their maximum weight in the late autumn.

Like the vixens, the dog foxes show an early summer drop in average weight. I can think of no obvious reason for this fall, except that male foxes are more heavily parasitised than females, and it is known that presence of sex hormones in the blood of an animal depresses the degree of parasitisation to which it is subject. During the rut, the presence of sex hormones in the dog-fox's blood will presumably keep parasites within reasonable limits, but after the rut this will no longer be the case and the number of parasites should, theoretically, begin to rise. This might account for the observed loss in weight of dog foxes.

It may, of course, be, as Lund suggests, that the number of specimens available for examination in the summer are not sufficient for reliable conclusions to be drawn, yet the correlation between a May low in England and a June low in Norway does seem to be more than coincidence. The smaller number available in the summer is due to a decline in hunting and the difficulty in warm weather of transporting bodies for examination from one part of the country to another. Lund suggests that the early summer loss in weight of both dog and vixen is due to nutritional pressures on the parents when feeding the cubs. It is suggested that the dog fox does capture food at this time but transfers it to the vixen and/or cubs. I very much doubt this theory, which is dealt with in some detail in the chapter, Fox Society, and think it more likely that the high incidence of mange and other parasites in April and May in England accounts for some of the loss in weight, as does a general change in habits, with the fox preferring to lie up and recover after the rut. Furthermore, if the dog were providing food for both cubs and vixen, one would not expect the latter's average weight to fall as greatly as it appears to do in early April.

In Norway, where mange is less common, the decline in weight of males in April and May (much less than the loss in England), cannot be due to this cause, and in England mange is probably a secondary rather than a primary factor.

Music and Movement

Foxes are credited with a wide variety of noises variously described as barks, yaps, screams and howls, and an even wider variety of descriptive terms, such as peacocks' screams and banshee yells. Some authors describe typical vixen and typical dog-fox calls; others claim that the noises made by both sexes are much the same and cannot be distinguished with certainty. Not only is there controversy about the noise made but also the significance of the sounds and the position adopted by the fox when delivering them. Does the fox howl from a sitting position, and does the so-called 'vixen screaming' take place during mating? So far as the free living fox is concerned, we are not really able to answer any of the questions with certainty, nor are we completely sure about which sex makes what noises and the significance of the different calls. Some country people claim that a fox is a mimic and can call rabbits or rats and even 'baa' like a sheep.

All I can do is to present a verbal picture of the sounds I have heard foxes make in the field and offer my own interpretation of their significance.

In view of the foregoing, it may seem odd to begin by saying that foxes are, for the most part, fairly silent animals. But when we recall that they are, in general, also solitary animals it begins to make sense. It is only when foxes show any form of social behaviour that they use their vocal powers.

By listening for foxes throughout the years of study and keeping detailed records of the times and kinds of noises heard, I have been able to build up what is really a pattern of noises typical of particular times of year, at least in this area. A diary of fox noises heard over a whole year is given in Appendix A.

Winter barking activity begins in lowland Gloucestershire about the middle of December and is intense about 6 pm, after which it is heard until approximately 9 pm with very little noise thereafter. Calls are of three main kinds, the commonest and most easily recognisable being a 'wo-wo' type of short, sharp bark. The number of phrases in the bark and their pitch seem to vary considerably between foxes, so that one is able to distinguish between individual voices. At Kent's Green, the three most vociferous foxes are, or at least were in the winter of 1965–6, the 'wo-wo' individual with a harsh deep voice, mentioned in the chapter, Watching Foxes, whose most common bark was a double note, although it also occasionally gave a triple bark; secondly a 'wo-wo-ough' fox—the last phrase ending in a rising, rather shrill, protracted shout (a note rather like the human 'ouch', after involuntary contact with a sharp object) from an animal I called 'the hysterical fox'; and the third a 'wo-wo-wo-wo' individual in which the bark was typical but much softer and of higher pitch than the 'wo-wo' fox bark.

The second type of December bark is the single, rather hollow utterance, best described as a yell 'wooooooooogh', the middle part being longer and of much higher pitch than the beginning and tailing off to a low note again at the end. The whole bark lasts about a second and the yell may be repeated at intervals of a few seconds or may be a single utterance.

The third, and much rarer type of noise, is a light yapping occasionally heard among the other noises. It sounds rather like a small terrier dog, and may be so in some cases as domestic dogs do join in the barking, although, in my experience, this is the exception rather than the rule. I also have records in my fieldbook of what I described as an hysterical screaming which lasts for a few seconds at a time and is rather like the noise of cats fighting. This comes at very irregular intervals and varies considerably in duration.

SCREAMING AND BARKING

I had my first close experience of this type of noise on 7 March 1965 when, between 8.15 and 8.45 pm, I listened to what I described in my fieldbook as two 'screaming fights, rather cat-like noises, but with a difference'. The position of what I took to be a running fight between at least two foxes changed as I listened, until the noise finally died away in the distance. The night was cold and frosty, so the sound travelled well. I did not hear similar noises again until 29 December 1965; it was a particularly wet evening with a strong wind from the east and I decided to listen for fox barks from the comfort of my Dormobile. I parked just off the lane near Savage's Grange Earth, during a break in the rain clouds which allowed the moon to shine through. After a few minutes, the same type of screaming and yelling that I had heard in March shattered the windy night for about thirty seconds. The noises all came from a point close to the earth and the animals making the noise moved quickly as they gave voice, although I could only follow their movements by ear. I suspected that two or more foxes were either fighting or mating; no other noises were heard that night despite a long, cold wait. It is not hard to imagine why people believe old buildings to be haunted if, as I did on that windy December night, they hear a fox screaming near the site of a once large house well away from the lights of civilisation.

My next opportunity to listen to screaming came on 31 January 1966, when it lasted for about three minutes and was repeated on 8 February. At the time, I described it as rather like listening to a duck being slowly and painfully strangled.

From observations made by Vincent (1958) on foxes coming to bait in Alaska, screaming has been claimed to be part of bloodless combat and I believe this is the explanation of many of the noises I heard from adults in winter and from cubs in the late summer and autumn. For cubs seem to be able to produce exactly the same type of screaming noises during their aggressive play activities. On a number of occasions I have watched cubs playing and screaming at one another, a particularly common occurrence in August, September and October.

Screaming does seem also to have something to do with mating, although usually, I think, it is intended to keep animals apart rather than to bring them together. As we know from Hurrell's reports, captive dog foxes can make noises equally as weird as those of the vixen, and he says there is no screaming during copulation. Film evidence from Norway, however, proves that the screaming I have described takes place both before and during copulation attempts.

As the screaming of foxes seems to occur frequently in October around Hallowe'en, I wonder just how much it may be responsible for the tales of ghostly noises and witches screams at this time of year.

I have heard the 'wo-wo' type of bark on only three occasions outside the winter months. The first was at Woodchester in May 1965, when two foxes were heard travelling down one side of a valley apparently calling to one another—rather a mixture of the 'wo-wo' and the yell calls. The second incident occurred in May 1966 at Savage's Grange Earth. I was getting near the earth, where I knew there were cubs, when I heard a soft 'owo-wo-wo' which I took to be the vixen warning the cubs of my approach. As the wind was blowing from the earth to me and the noise came down wind, I knew I could not have been detected by scent. Moving slowly forward, with pauses, hoping to catch a glimpse of the fox, I again heard the soft call. About thirty feet from the earth, I saw a cub walking about rather restlessly; again I heard the call very close by and could not understand why the cub was still above ground if this was, in fact, an alarm note. Although the ground around the earth was slightly undulating, I had an extremely good view of the surrounding area and was sure that no adult fox could have concealed itself from me.

The mystery was solved when the cub, after momentarily disappearing into some long grass, suddenly appeared on a trail that would bring it almost to where I stood. It came on at a good trot with its small tail held low and the barks now sounded very close indeed. Veering slightly, the cub went out of sight into some thick scrub just behind me, but soon reappeared in front of me and barked 'owo-wo-wo'. So small cubs *can* bark like adults, and this cub was only about five weeks old. The cub's movements suggested it was hunting for something and I can only imagine it was calling in the hope that an adult would provide food, for it certainly was not aware of my presence. No other cubs were seen that evening, although subsequently I found there were four living at that earth.

The third occasion on which I heard this 'wo-wo' type of bark was actually prior to the one just described but the significance, or rather the interpretation, of what I heard could not be deduced until after the cub incident. I had been watching cubs at Savage's Little Pond

Earth during the first week of May 1966 and on one evening, when visual observations were no longer possible because of the poor light, there was so much activity still going on and occasional noises from the cubs that I sat tight, just listening. It was quite an exercise trying to interpret what was going on from the sounds of rapid to and fro movements in the vegetation. Then I heard the 'wo-wo-wo' softly from the field just above the earth, echoed by a similar call from the earth entrance area. This apparent conversation went on for several minutes and I then thought it was a dialogue between the two parents who might have come to visit the cubs. But in the light of my experience at Grange Earth, I now think that those soft 'wo-wo-wos' were made by the cubs at this earth. These are the only occasions I have heard cubs vocalise in this way.

I think the 'wo-wo' type of bark is used mainly, but by no means exclusively, by dog foxes in winter. The question can only be resolved with certainty by observing foxes of known sex producing the bark and, since foxes bark mainly at night, this would be very difficult. I have heard occasional fox barks in daylight, as on the Cotswolds at 4.15 pm on 14 January 1966, when I heard a warbled 'wo-oo-wo' which was repeated softly several times—a very feminine voice for a fox? From oscillograph records, Tembrock claims that rhythmic calls are socially positive, so perhaps this warble call was a contact note. The 'woooooooough', or howl, heard in winter is also a commonly heard fox sound in spring and summer. I have recorded it in February, March, June, July, August, September and October.

On 5 June 1966, I was returning home up the fields after a long and non-productive watch in Savage's Orchard when, as I neared Clewes' Pond Earth, I heard a piercing howl from the orchard. The noise was repeated six times with a brief pause in between and though it was still fairly light I failed to see the fox that was producing this disturbance. The time was 10.15 pm, just about when, as we have seen earlier, the vixen comes to the cubs, and I assume the howls were the mother's long-range warning to the cubs at the earth. A similar sound was heard on a number of occasions that summer, often just before nightfall. It lasted for only a few seconds, the howl being repeated up to a dozen times.

Although we live entirely surrounded by fields and foxes we are seldom awakened by them at night, except in June and July, and it is always the single repeated howl note we hear. Twice my wife and I have been almost shot out of bed by a sudden ear-piercing shriek from just outside our bedroom window. On both occasions the night was extremely still, with brilliant moonlight. On the second occasion the fox was so close that we tried to shoo it away before it woke up our small boys; we could hear it moving through the grass in the orchard opposite and make out every detail of its bark. Heard at this short range, the howl can be divided into three 'wo-wo-wo's' repeated so rapidly that they slur almost into one. The pitch and volume rise rapidly with the third 'wo' and it ends in a high, hollow-sounding, terror-inducing note, most inadequately described as an 'oooough'. Heard at a distance, the preliminary notes are not often discernible and only the 'ooooough' carries to the listener. Is the purpose of the noise to induce terror, as it could well do or is its main purpose to sound a warning, perhaps off human habitations? I do not think it is a 'beware of human habitation' cry, for foxes regularly visit such locations; much more likely that the vixen is warning off her cubs from their former home area as the family breaks up and disperses. If this is so, then the same call which, only the month before, was being used to warn the cubs of danger, is now used against them. Tembrock (1962) claims that the meaning of sounds and other behaviour patterns are determined by the conditions under which they occur. We may thus have a good example here of one sound having different meanings, depending upon the age of the cubs.

The terrier-like yapping I have mentioned sometimes occurs in winter but, probably because the call is quite soft and does not travel any distance, I have not heard it very often. A bark similar to the cub bark is also heard from adults in winter and it is best described as a yodel bark. It usually consists of three phrases slurred together, again basically a 'wo-wo' type bark but with the emphasis on the 'oo' rather than the 'ww'. In my fieldbook, I represent this bark as 'OwOwOwO'. This, like the yapping bark, is soft and what I call the contact call. During the mating season the dog fox is either travelling with or very close to the vixen and a stentorian call such as the 'wo-wo' or yell would seem to be quite superfluous and probably highly dangerous to the mated pair. It seems much more likely that the soft calls are the contact-making calls, the others being aggressive calls with the opposite intention of avoiding contact.

I heard another variation of bark, also, I think, a contact call, on a clear, frosty night with a full moon on 28 October 1966. At 11 pm a fox was heard in Woodman's Orchard—'Qwqwqwqwqwqwwooh' barks were repeated with a few seconds' pause in between, each phrase lasting about two seconds. The number of 'qwqw's' varied, sometimes only two or three being repeated softly and without a final rising 'wooh'. I would not think the sounds carried very far, as some were very soft indeed. The long phrase sounded vaguely similar to a rapid duck-like quacking, slowly rising to a crescendo with the final 'wooh'. About ten minutes later and from the same direction came single yells and the sound of distant fighting accompanied by loud yells.

Most of the calls so far mentioned have been variations on the 'wo-wo' theme, but there are two other noises that foxes produce which cannot be so described and which are seldom heard. I have already mentioned the occasions when I heard vixens produce distinct hiccups, a noise that can be reproduced by saying the word at the back of the throat softly, drawing in quickly for the 'hic' and breathing out in a more relaxed manner on the 'cup'. When I first heard the noise I thought that the three or four hiccups given softly near the earth were the 'all clear' sign, but two later incidents taught me that this is a warning signal from the adult to the cubs when danger is detected. It is a soft note that will not carry far and is only of use when the cubs are with, or very close to, the adults. I have implied that both sexes produce this noise, though my only evidence is for the vixen. The hiccup noise is preceded by a guttural growl of short duration.

I have read that foxes can bleat like a lost lamb, squeal like an injured rabbit or squeak to charm rats from farm buildings. This may be so, but I cannot vouch for the validity of the claims and also think that the noise made by fighting cubs and adults could well be taken for mimicry of a rabbit. It is said that the purpose of this mimicry is to lure a victim to the fox's jaws or, in the case of sheep away from their young, but if this is really so I wonder why foxes bother to eat such trifles as beetles and worms and spend so much time catching voles. And, perhaps more significantly, why are so few rat remains found in fox stomachs or droppings? Rats are, after all, cosmopolitan, yet are seldom eaten.

CUB NOISES

Cubs, as we have seen, do make some noise, but their early play is much more silent than that of badger cubs. They tend to be noisier when the vixen is with the cubs for the evening romp and yapping can then be heard.

In July and August there is much vocal activity from the cubs at sunset. Just before they emerge from the hedgerows in which they are now living, the noise is rather like cats fighting, with much screaming. At other times I have thought I was listening to two brown owls fighting until the occasional sharp yap and screams made the sound identifiable and on a number of occasions I was able to confirm this by actually watching and listening at the same time. When making these noises the cubs perform leaping, stiff-legged, rather cat-like movements and there is always much chasing. They seem to do this each evening, either just before or just after emerging, which gives me a useful check on activity time in the summer, even though I may not see the cubs producing the noises.

In October 1966, cubs were heard at approximately 5 am. First there was a 'tch, tch,' noise—rather like a badger or a blackbird. Feet could be heard prancing around in the frosty grass of the orchard, and then the 'tch's' came very near and were repeated very rapidly. At the same time there was a loud, short squealing, rather like a rabbit caught in a gin trap. There were at least two individuals present and they might have been fighting like the cubs I heard in August, alternatively this might have been mating 'play' (Plate 7a). The 'tch, tch' call is, I think, the call of an angry fox.

There are doubtless many other noises produced by the fox for various purposes. Hurrell describes a rapidly repeated guttural noise, rather like a purr. This, he says, is made by the vixen when she returns to the earth with food, and he suggests that it is an 'all clear' signal. Yet although I have watched at earths for many hours and have seen vixens return to their cubs, I have never heard this noise. Indeed, it is seldom necessary for the vixen to call them as the cubs usually wait for her at the entrance to or outside the earth, or even run across a field to greet her.

Foxes are said to bark at the moon and certainly there does seem to be more vocal activity on cold, clear moonlight nights than on other occasions. This may be partly explained by sound travelling more easily under these conditions, or it may represent an actual increase. If we remember that scent is the foxes' main method of communicating with one another and that on cold frosty evenings scenting conditions are bad, it may well be that, under such conditions, they do use vocal communication methods rather than 'scent newspapers'. In general, however, I have found that foxes will bark under all atmospheric conditions in the winter months, though one is not always then prepared to go out and listen for them.

MOVEMENT

A moving fox is most people's first sight of the animal and the movement most usually seen is a galloping flight. In its normal perambulation about its home range a fox moves at a trot, with short rather jerky movements frequently punctuated by a stop to sniff at or paw something that may be edible. When watched in grassland or orchards, the path taken by a searching fox is very complicated with zigzags, back-tracks and loops. There usually seems to be a general direction of movement, however, and this is into the wind. General searching movements seem to be used to locate invertebrate prey such as slugs and beetles, and also to find fallen fruit. The head is held low, the tail droops and on a number of occasions I have been able to get a sustained view of the fox, and even to follow it at a distance, provided I moved only when the animal's head was sniffing out some delicacy from the base of a grass root.

When in a hurry the fox gallops along at a good pace of up to thirty-five miles an hour. The hind footprint will be found ahead of the front footprint and prints will be found in groups of four about four feet apart. The fox gallops with head up and brush held low, moving along in a rather bounding, untidy gait.

When stalking prey, it adopts a cat-like approach with body held close to the ground, legs rather cramped up beneath the body, nose down, and ears very erect and forward pointing. A characteristic track is left by such activities consisting of closely bunched footprints, probably ending at a final leaping point.

I have only once seen a fox walk slowly and this was during scenting, as described in the chapter on Fox Society. The fox then walked with a decidedly stiff-legged action, almost a 'goose step' jerkily executed, with the crooked tail held aloft (Plate 7b), presumably to expose the anal scent glands for action. Movement of this type is described by ethologists as posturing. Typical postures are often associated with many forms of behaviour and seem to be a means by which animals communicate their mood or intentions to one another. In the instance I witnessed, however, posturing was performed in the absence of any other fox.

Tree-climbing is often mentioned in books about the hunted fox but this is really little more than the ability to run up a steeply sloping lower branch, with a possible final leap into a convenient fork. During an afternoon walk in January 1966 I disturbed a fox lying up in a pollarded willow about eight feet above the ground. The fox, which had a dark tail tag, ran down the broken branch that had given it access to the willow and galloped off across a winter wheat field. I investigated the lying-up place but found only a collection of wind-blown leaves and gale-torn twigs, forming a temporary resting place in the January afternoon sun.

The characteristic high leap of the fox when hunting voles or mice always reminds me of the play movement so commonly seen among cubs from July onwards and also shown by adults. The play pounce is more stiff-legged than the mouse pounce but both are basically the same movement. Play pounce in cubs is, as I shall explain later, probably an aggressive movement, just as with the adults it seems to. be a ritualised fight. Two animals perform a circular leaping 'dance', accompanied by wild shrieking and this is particularly prevalent during the breeding season, which is about the only time of year when adults come into physical proximity.

After a slight fall of snow in January 1965, I found evidence of much fox activity near Big Pit. Many trails were clearly visible and it was very noticeable that they crossed time and time again, forming figure-of-eight patterns and circles in the snow. These I interpreted as being produced during a mating chase.

Tail movements do not seem to be of great significance in the fox when compared with the variety of expressions, pleasurable or otherwise, that can be deduced from observing the position and movement of a dog's tail. During the scenting incident I watched, the fox's tail was held crooked high over its back, a similar position to that seen when territorial disputes are taking place, as is well shown in Plate 7b. Reports of dog foxes chasing a vixen in Russia mention that the dogs held their tails high aloft, presumably in the same position as in scenting and fighting. Tail-raising would seem, therefore, to be associated with socially important activities and probably indicative of an aggressive mood in the fox.

The only occasion I have seen the tail moved sideways was during a playful romp performed by a cub in Savage's Orchard. The movements of this cub were most cat-like as it raced around, twisting from side to side and then lying with feet outspread while its tail lashed from side to side.

We must, I fear, discount as fiction the fox's supposed use of its tail as a fishing aid, though it has been said that a fox will dip its brush into a stream to catch crayfish which are supposed to cling to it. Some crayfish, some fox!

Foxes are, however, extremely good swimmers, although I have not observed this myself and am inclined to think that a fox will not normally go into water if it can possibly avoid it. Many readers will no doubt recall the story about the fox's alleged method of ridding itself of fleas. The fox is said to take a tuft of grass or wool in its mouth and to walk slowly backwards into a pond or stream until only the tip of the snout holding the wool or grass is above water level. Meanwhile, the fleas are supposed to move down to the head end of the fox on to the tuft which the animal then releases, so disposing of the fleas. It is a delightful story but seems highly unlikely for a number of reasons, of which we need mention only two. Fleas normally live close to the skin of the fox among the dense underfur which contains much trapped air. For the fleas to suffer any discomfort by water, the whole pelt would have to be completely saturated, a lengthy process that would cause more discomfort to the fox than a large number of fleas. The second point concerns the supposed migration of the fleas against the grain of the hair. By the time the fleas had moved to the tips of the guard hairs, as they do when an animal host dies, they would be well under water with little chance of gaining their objective.

A cub's exploratory movements are very much like those seen in domestic cats and dogs. On encountering a novel object in its environment, a cub's first reaction is often to take a rapid, stiff-legged backwards leap with ears held well back (Plate 8a). This is followed by a few seconds' pause then, with snout down and fore paw ready to prod, the cub slowly approaches and, after two or three slight withdrawals, sniffs the object. If the object does not move, the cub attempts to encourage it to do so by a gentle sideways swipe with its paw. If this succeeds the cub will leap backwards again and repeat the performance. An unresponsive object will probably be chewed and either eaten or rejected. Should the cub's activities cause an animate object to move away rapidly the cub will quickly snap at it and, if edible, it will be eaten.

Foxes are most subject to human observation during the hunt and natural history books abound with stories of the devices they use to confuse the pursuing hounds. It is not proposed to recount any of the well-known stories but simply to point out again that these devices are not necessarily produced by conscious thought on the part of the fox. Many animals, when pursued, will double back on their trails, which may or may not confuse the pursuer but is nothing more than the automatic reaction of an animal which is being chased. A hare will adopt much the same tactics as a fox in trying to escape dogs, but few people would rank the hare very high in the mammalian intelligence scale.

Nor is it necessary to assume that the fox leads the hounds to water knowing that, by jumping over it, its trail will be broken. Water jumps are much used in the breeding season, as we have seen, so what more natural than that the fox should use these well-established routes when being pursued by hounds? The broken trail is merely the result of the fox following its normal practice when going along a stream or river, and if it also results in the safety of the fox, so much the better for the survival of the individual and the species.

Diet

A quick glance at a fox's teeth should be sufficient to tell us why it is classified as a carnivorous animal. In the photograph of an open-mouthed vixen (Plate 8b) it will be seen that the teeth are very much like those of a dog, which is not surprising since both animals belong to the same family, *Canidae*, together with wolves, jackals and other dog-like carnivores.

A fox has forty-two teeth, of which those in half a jaw are represented by the following dental formula:

Upper Jaw: incisors 3, canines 1, premolars 4, molars 2, $\left.\right\} \times 2 = 42$
Lower Jaw: incisors 3, canines 1, premolars 4, molars 3,

When examining a fox skull, it will be noticed that the long upper canine teeth project a little below the lower part of the bottom jaw.

1a *View from Big Pit looking towards the Rutting Trail*

1b *Big Pit with "Look-Out Earth" beneath the tree roots*

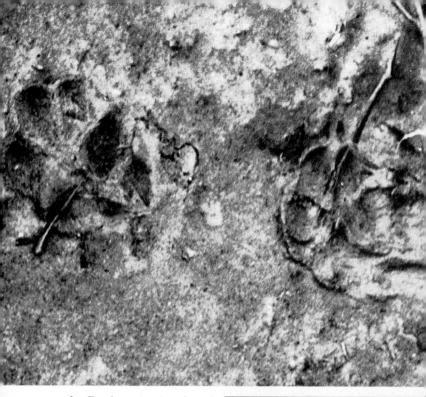

2a *Fox footprints in soft earth*

2b *Forefoot of a vixen*

3a *Badger Earth, Big Pit: an old badger skull has been excavated by the resident fox*

3b *Foxes dig out their earths in October*

4a *A fox trail*

4b *Cub trails often lead to play or feeding areas of flattened grass*

5a *Young fox: the black eye stripes and the gland on the dorsal surface of the tail are well defined*

5b *Cub scats on flattened grass*

6a *The field vole or short-tailed vole* (Microtus agrestis), *an important fox food*

6b *Head of a young fox in bright light: note the vertical slit-like pupils*

7a Dog fox and vixen in open-mouthed courtship display

7b Captive dog foxes engaged in a territorial dispute:
Second dog just visible beneath. Not position of the tail

8a *Fox cub in exploration posture*

8b *Open-mouthed courtship display of a captive vixen*

9a *Typical fox posture when chewing prey*

9b *Two cubs awaiting return of vixen*

10a *The yellow-necked mouse* (Apodemus flavicollis) *which, like the woodmouse* (Apodemus Sylvaticus) *is sometimes dug out*

10b *The brown rat* (Rattus norvegicus) *a plentiful but little used source of fox food in Gloucestershire*

11a *Tame dog-fox cub playing with domestic dog*

11b *Captive dog fox in screaming position*

12a *Dog fox bringing food to a vixen – in captivity*

12b *Fox cub about four weeks old*

13a *Cub about six weeks old*

13b *Cubs may be seen out-side their earths during most daylight hours in May*

14a *Fox and badger, our two largest carnivores, whose paths must often cross*

14b *Young rabbits made up a considerable proportion of fox prey in pre-myxomatosis days*

15a *Dog fox*

15b *Foxes are common in countryside greatly influenced by man*

16 *Young fox: there is still much to be learned by direct observation
of the wild red fox*

This is a typical feature of a red-fox skull and helps to distinguish it from that of a dog or other type of fox in which the upper canines are not so long proportionately.

For an animal with such a powerful set of teeth, one would expect animal food to be the most important part of its diet, and this deduction as we shall see, is accurate when the total diet is considered over a whole year.

FOOD ANALYSIS

I found that the best way to learn about the eating habits of the local foxes was to collect and analyse fox droppings in the manner I have already described. Yet when friends have asked me about my work on Gloucestershire foxes, most have been shocked and some horrified that I should even contemplate looking for scats, let alone find out what is inside them. Far too many people who claim to be interested in wild animals prefer to close their eyes to much that is of vital importance in their lives. I recall a naturalist programme on the BBC in 1966, when Tony Soper, Devera Klineman, of the London Zoo, and myself were discussing foxes' and other carnivores' scenting and defecating habits; one of the critics who reviewed the programme went so far as to question the maturity of three speakers who could talk about such topics! A layman is obviously entitled to his opinions but to criticise three naturalists for talking about animals in actuality rather than as children's picture-book characters, is absurd.

Vital functions in any animal are eating, reproducing, breathing and getting rid of waste or unused products from the body in the form of urine (or uric acid) and faeces or scats, respectively. Faeces, which are composed of unused fragments of food, are often of great importance to mammals. As is now well known, rabbits produce two types of droppings, a hard round 'marble' and a soft night dropping. The latter are not usually seen, however, as the rabbit eats them as soon as they emerge from the anus. This habit, known as coprophagy, is of importance to the rabbit in obtaining substances which would otherwise be wasted, in particular vitamins. The coprophagous habit is also found in a number of other animals, including the fox and the dog.

Droppings from herbivorous animals are usually not of unpleasant odour to the human nose, which is more than can be said for those from omnivorous and particularly carnivorous animals. In the case of the latter, the smell is imparted by a secretion from the anal glands.

Droppings from some herbivorous animals, such as the rhinoceros and hippopotamus, are used by the animal to mark out a territory and this is also often the case with the carnivores, including the fox. The scented dropping is, therefore, useful as a means of social communication in animals and an all-important field sign since it seems to be a vital part of the animal's way of life, which is precisely what a true naturalist should be trying to decipher. To refuse to look at droppings is to act rather like a detective investigating a murder who refuses to examine the body because he cannot bring himself to look at blood. I cannot say that droppings are the most aesthetically pleasing of objects to deal with, but if one is going to discover fact, as opposed to advancing theories about the fox's way of life and its feeding habits in particular, then they must be studied.

The scats I collected each week were all in very fresh condition and broke up easily when washed well in running water after being placed in a very fine sieve. Any particles that passed through the sieve I collected and examined microscopically for earthworm bristles or chaetae.

After a thorough wash the remains were seen to be simply bits of bone, fur, fruit, grass, insects and pieces of whatever the fox had eaten within the last few hours. From work done on blue foxes in captivity, we know that a fox begins to defecate between eight and ten hours after feeding, the most frequent time being between sixteen and twenty hours after food. Food remains in the stomach, where it is subject to attack by stomach acids, for over two and a half hours, during which some of the bones and teeth of small mammals and the feathers of birds are partially dissolved.

The washed remains from the sieve were then tipped into an enamel dish with clean water and the remains sorted with forceps and mounted needles. Fur, bones and teeth were separated out and placed on blotting paper, after which the bits were identified. The hairs were at first the most difficult item to identify but I later produced my own reference collection of hairs from known mammals, and was thus able to construct a simple key for the recognition of hairs found in the scats. The easiest method of identification was to section the different hairs using a needle and cotton, a cork and a razor blade, and this technique is described in Appendix H.

Teeth of small mammals were easily identified after a little practice but cannot alone be relied upon to identify small rodent prey for Lund has shown in feeding tests that the molars of *Microtus sp.* are more easily broken down by the digestive juices in the fox's intestine and stomach than are the molars of *Apodemus*. It seems that only about 45 per cent of the teeth of small rodents appears in the scats of fox and coyote (Lockie, 1959, and Murie, 1956).

During my analyses I often commented in my notes on the absence of *Microtus* teeth and limb bones, although I found abundant hair on which to base my identification. This dissolving action may be the reason why I have seldom found tail or other vertebrae in scats containing other rodent remains. Skull fragments are also rare, the only hard parts of the head preserved usually being the upper and lower molar area of the jaws. If only about half the remains of small rodents fed to a fox appear in the droppings, then my estimation of the importance of small mammals in the Kent's Green foxes' diet may have to be increased by a factor of two.

When I came to identify bird remains in the form of quill bases, down feathers and—a most characteristic remain—the complete skin from a bird's foot, minus foot bones but with the claws still attached, I found much more difficulty. Bird remains can be identified from the feathers, as has been shown recently by Day (1966) for weasel droppings, but I did not attempt species identification and in many cases could not identify birds further than their families. On a number of occasions bird eggshell was found—though how this survived the stomach acidity I do not know—and I was once even able to identify an egg fragment as being either starling or hedge ascentor.

Identification of fruit remains was straightforward once I discovered characteristic features of each fruit eaten. Pear remains are typically gritty, due to the presence of numerous stone cells in the flesh. The roughcast nature of the flesh side of the pear skin, together with a characteristic stalk with long plume of fibres and cone-like remains of the calyx, also aid positive identification. Apple remains, by contrast, have smooth skin on the flesh side and lack the gritty texture in the flesh. Plum stones and skin are quite easily identified, as are cherry stones, acorns and the red arils and skins of yew berries. Other vegetation, such as grass, straw, leaves and bits of moss, were not identified further than these general headings.

Invertebrate remains were identified from the hard parts of the exoskeleton, which remain virtually untouched after digestion. Beetle elytra, antennae and legs enabled family recognition to be made, and even species to be identified in some cases. Larvae of *Dipterus* and *Lepidopterus* insects were often found as empty skins giving ghost-like remains, lacking colour but still with the head intact.

The only trace of earthworms I found were the golden yellow chaetae which are easily picked out, together with the sand or soil from their gut contents, under the low power of a microscope. Sand has often been found in fox stomachs and scats, particularly with young animals, but very few workers seem to have looked in the sand for earthworm chaetae. Usually, when I have found large quantities of soil or sand in scats, I felt sure it originated mainly from the fox's habit of eating worms, although doubtless some is taken accidentally. When earthworm chaetae appeared in scats at the same time as bird remains, I assumed that the worms were from the bird's gut contents.

Mollusc remains were rare; only occasionally did I find small snail shells and these, I think, were eaten by mistake and were unbroken. Slugs are eaten a great deal, as I have confirmed from visual observations of adults feeding, and though their soft bodies do not survive stomach acidity and digestive juices, the contents of their digestive gland, fortunately, do. When I found a 'vegetable soup-like' material in a dropping, I attributed it to slug gut contents.

All the items in the foxes' diet can thus be recognised either directly or, as with slugs, indirectly, and by examining a sufficient number of faeces it is possible to get a very good qualitative estimation of the foxes' diet. These qualitative results I collected together each month of my survey and plotted the various food items as percentage occurrences of the total number of scats analysed for each month (Figs 10a and b).

This method, of necessity, gives a rather distorted picture of the relative importance of each item in the total diet. For example, a single caterpillar skin and the remains of a rabbit would, if present in a single dropping, both count as one occurrence of implied equal volume importance. In an attempt, therefore, to put my analysis on a more realistic quantitative basis, I prepared another diagram after giving a volume number to each food item found in each scat. If a large amount of the particular food item was present in a scat, it was given a score of five, a moderate amount scored three and a trace, only one. While this is a crude approximation to a quantitative analysis, the results are, I feel, much nearer to giving a realistic

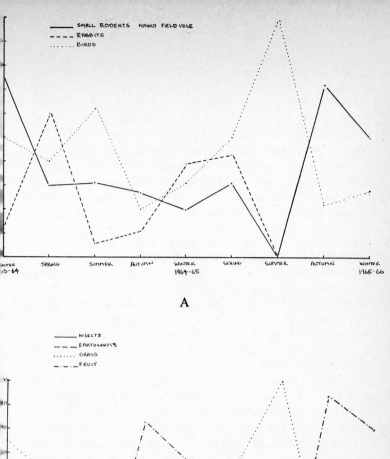

A

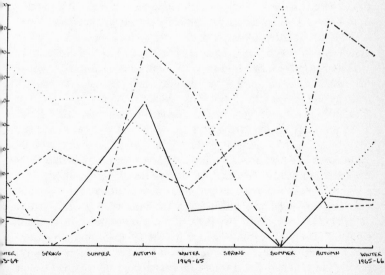

B

10a. & 10b. Graphs showing qualitative analysis of food

picture of the relative importance of each food item in the foxes' diet (Figs 11a and b).

THE DIET OF THE ADULT

Wherever possible, I collected or had brought to me the bodies of foxes killed on local roads or caught in snares, and an analysis of the gut contents of these animals helped to supplement the information I obtained from droppings. The numbers of droppings collected varied tremendously with the month of the year, even though I intensified my visits to the collecting area when fewer were available. I consider the number of droppings found each month to be indicative of fox activity, and hence the number of foxes in the area. Thus droppings, together with other sign, can be used to obtain a rough idea of population density of foxes in an area.

I discovered that there was a marked fluctuation over the seasons in the amount of fox predation on mammals. Rabbits and hares were common in the area I studied until January 1965, when the local rabbit population completely disappeared after a resurgence of myxomatosis. No live rabbits were seen after January. Hares, however, being immune, continued to be as, or more common than before the disease. During my visits to the breeding earths in 1964 I found hare remains consisting of the complete pelvic girdle with hind limb bones still attached. This seemingly characteristic type of hare, and for that matter rabbit remains, seems to be produced by the activities of the cubs who, being unable to crack the bones, simply suck and rasp the meat from them. Hare fur was occasionally found in scats, usually in spring, but the vast majority of *Langomorph* (rabbits and hares) remains were of rabbit.

After January 1965, very few *Langomorph* remains were found and most probably derived from carrion. Myxomatosis, together with fox predation, has eliminated the rabbit from this small area of Gloucestershire and probably any recolonisation of the area will be prevented, or at least retarded, by the resident fox population.

When the rabbits disappeared, hares were not turned to as might have been expected, probably because the hare is too fast and skilful in removing itself from the jaws of the fox, at least in lowland England. The same cannot be said for the Scottish mountain hare, which frequently occurs in the mountain fox diet, while in Norway, during the summer, Lund found that hare remains occurred much more frequently in vixens' stomachs than in dog foxes'.

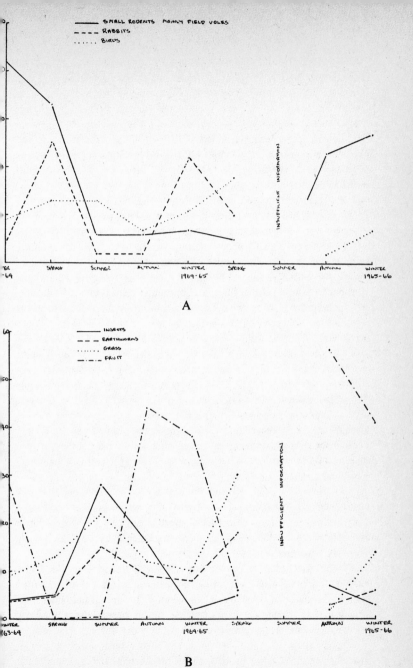

11a. & 11 b. Graphs showing quantitative analysis of food

Before the arrival of myxomatosis and in the bad old days of gin traps, rabbit was probably the staple diet of the fox; what he could not catch for himself (which would be mainly young and senile), he stole from the gins. The vast quantity of fur one finds in droppings after a fox has had a rabbit meal makes it obvious the fox does not skin before consumption and leaves little of the carcass. I have found claws, teeth and all the bones of the rabbit appearing in bits in various scats. However, it is said that the ears and tail are not consumed and this may be so.

I had only completed one full year's analysis before the rabbits disappeared and so my remarks about seasonal predation on them refer only to 1964 and not to subsequent years of the study. Rabbit would seem to be an important item in the foxes' diet in autumn, winter and early spring, and to be almost non-existent in summer when, presumably, the rabbit population is at its greatest and the number of young rabbits high, an apparently anomalous situation.

The field vole, *Microtus agrestis*, is the only vole to feature in the fox diet from the area I studied, although there are reports of both bank vole, *Clethrionomys glareolus*, and water vole, *Arvicola terrestris*, being taken when available (Abashkin, 1963). Both were potential food for the fox in my area but I did not find any trace of them in the droppings. *Microtus* remains were most commonly found in autumn and winter, with another period of importance in April when the cubs have to be fed. Teeth, limb bones and other skeletal remains often occur in a much divided state (Plate 9a), indicating that the fox chews even such small prey and does not swallow them whole as is often stated (Fig 12). I think it probably significant that I found very few tail vertebrae in the vole remains. In the winter of 1965 I found the remains of a field vole that had been excavated near its runway by the fox; they consisted of bits of hair, a hind foot and, what was of most interest to me, a tail. These two pieces of evidence would seem to indicate that at least some foxes reject parts of voles on occasions.

Typical fox mousing or voleing technique has already been described and excavated vole runways are commonly found in rough pasture lands or in the rough at the sides of ploughed fields. In early autumn, fox droppings can often be found beside the ripped-out runway system, so proving that this is fox work rather than badger.

The diagram on page 106 (Fig 13) shows how, after myxomatosis had removed the rabbits, the Kent's Green foxes turned their

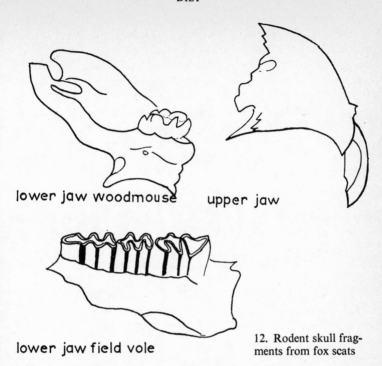

lower jaw woodmouse   upper jaw

lower jaw field vole

12. Rodent skull frag-
ments from fox scats

attention to small mammals, the vast majority being field voles. Autumn seems to be the time of greatest predation on small rodents, both when rabbits were available and in their absence. In October 1965, as will be seen, 84 per cent of the scats examined contained small mammal remains; in the corresponding month in 1964, when rabbits were available, they occurred only in 32 per cent, but this was still the peak occurrence for the year.

The diagram also brings out another point of interest. During 1964 there were three cub families on the Kent's Green land and many of the autumn scats collected, particularly in October, were droppings of young animals. In 1965, I saw only one family of two cubs that lived on the study area for but a few weeks. The autumn of that year produced a much smaller number of droppings, particularly in October when only six were collected against sixty-five in 1964. The smaller number in 1965 was composed mainly of adult droppings. It will be seen, therefore, that adult predation on voles

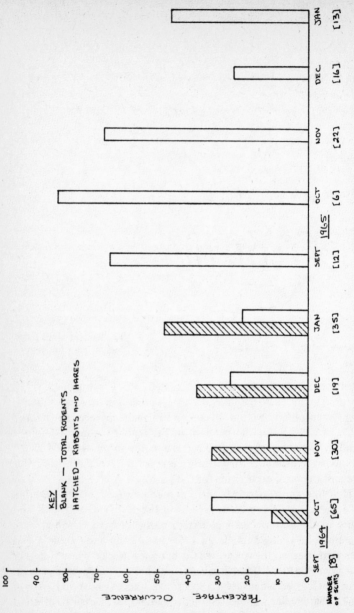

13. Histogram showing mammal occurence in the fox diet before and after myxomatosis affected the Kent's Green study area

would seem to be greater in autumn than that of cubs but, of course, many more analyses would have to be made to prove this point, and one would need to have rabbits as a constantly available and not variable food supply, as in the present case. It may even be that the decline in the local rabbit population temporarily reduced the breeding fox population.

The number of voles eaten by foxes during autumn and winter is probably large and this applies also to the spring if cubs are to be fed, as they were in 1964 when occurrence in droppings was high. Fewer voles are eaten in spring, such as in 1965, when there is an absence or shortage of cubs.

Lund found that the average weight of stomach contents from 316 foxes in Norway was 32 gm when dry. Seventeen weighed over 100 gm and one 253 gm. Wet weight of stomach contents would be about 100 gm (Hoffman & Kirkpatrick). In the scats I have analysed, only on rare occasions have the remains of more than one small rodent been found. On two or three occasions I did find *Microtus* remains together with those of the woodmouse, *Apodemus*. Probably in areas with a greater *Microtus* population than Kent's Green, one would find multiple remains of small rodents much more frequently. There are records quoted by Ognev of one fox stomach containing the remains of between forty and sixty voles and Collett (1911–12) records a collection of sixteen field mice (? *Microtus*) in the jaws of a fox which was shot while going to its earth. One vole per stomach in winter was Lund's findings, and my average of one vole per scat in autumn agrees well with this.

If food stays in the fox's stomach for approximately two and a half hours, as we have seen, and the fox hunts for about twelve hours in late autumn when it is preying on voles to its greatest extent for the year, we can expect an individual fox to eat about five voles a day. The five would weigh about 150 gm but we know that a fox needs to eat about a pound (450–500 gm) of food a day, which provides it with between 500 and 600 calories. So, even at times of peak predation on voles, the bulk of the food is derived from other sources, mainly fruit and birds when rabbits are not available. This amount of predation cannot have very much effect on the total vole population when it is possible to have over 100 voles per acre without real overcrowding taking place.

Of other small rodents, the only one to occur in the local foxes' diet was the woodmouse or long-tailed field mouse, *Apodemus sylvaticus.* I was not able to distinguish between remains of the common woodmouse, *A. sylvaticus*, and its close relative the yellow-necked mouse, *A. flavicollis* (Plate 10a), although these did occur at Kent's Green and were often trapped in the early winter, particularly in 1966 when five specimens were taken in as many days in our cottage.

Remains of woodmouse were not commonly found, occurring only eleven times during the study period and suggesting that they are more important as prey items to the fox in autumn and early winter. I was, however, able to find excavated woodmouse runways in field margins and hedgebottoms. The bones of the victims recovered from scats were always in a crushed state, as with *Microtus*, and again the absence of the tail vertebrae was marked. I have not found detached woodmouse tails but suspect that the fox, when it does catch a woodmouse, may not bother to eat this part of the anatomy, not surprisingly in view of its bony, sinuous nature.

Using live traps, I occasionally checked to see what were the most commonly occurring small rodents in the area at particular seasons. Always the woodmouse was the most commonly trapped animal and it seems strange that such a frequently occurring animal should not figure more prominently in the local fox diet. I have briefly mentioned possible reasons for this in the final chapter.

Another very common animal both in the hedges and local farms is the rat, *Rattus norvegicus* (Plate 10b). But again, as with the woodmouse, availability is by itself no guarantee of consumption by the local foxes. Remains were found on only fifteen occasions; these occurred in late autumn and winter when molar teeth and sheared off pieces of jaw bone were found together with rat hair in scats. In only one area where fox diet has been studied have rats been shown to make up a significant part of the diet.

The only other rodent to appear in the Kent's Green fox diet was the grey squirrel, the only species now found in Gloucestershire. Squirrel remains were recorded in three cub droppings in May 1965, and from two adults in January 1966. As with the bank vole, woodmouse and rat, the squirrel is rarely eaten, despite its availability to the fox. The grey squirrel spends much of its time on the ground in the autumn but, presumably, the fox is not normally able to catch or does not go out of its way to capture this very fleet-of-foot rodent. Other foods are more easily procured, except when the local farmers' squirrel shoot provides the fox with an easy meal, probably the origin of the squirrel remains I found.

Other mammals available to the fox but seldom eaten are the so-called insectivores—the mole, shrew and hedgehog; these seldom occur on the fox menu. Moles occurred only three times in adult droppings, once in July and twice in October 1964. I collected two freshly-killed moles from outside Clewes' Pond Earth in that year. One May afternoon I visited the earth and found the still warm body of a large mole near the earth entrance. There was no mark to be seen on it and as *rigor mortis* had not set in the vixen had presumably brought this offering to the cubs not many minutes before my arrival. A few days later a second body was found in the same spot. In the same month, remains of a mole were found outside Slope Earth in Big Pit and mole hair was later discovered in droppings of the cubs that lived there.

Moles were certainly quite common in the local fields but were more prevalent in 1964 than at any other time; I think it significant that this was the year when most mole remains were found associated with foxes. It seems that if other food is available the fox will not eat mole from choice, although it is thought good enough ballast for cubs.

Shrews were abundant, pygmy and water shrews being found both dead and alive at various times of the year. Water shrews live in the pond at Clewes' Pond Earth and, during early morning watches at this earth in May, I sometimes saw these noisy black and white animated motor boats within a few feet of the earth. But again, despite availability, I recorded shrew remains only three times in droppings; twice in November and once in December. Feeding tests (Lund) have shown that when other small mammals are available these are preferred to shrews.

The prickles of the hedgehog do not prevent the fox from opening up and devouring the soft underparts, leaving a cleaned skin to indicate the fatal encounter. Hedgehogs, it seems, are occasionally pushed into shallow water and forced to unroll, so becoming vulnerable to the fox's jaws. I found two cleaned hedgehog skins, one very close to Pond Earth and in whose pond the fatal bite was probably inflicted. No quills were found in any of the droppings, although these have occasionally been recorded by other workers. Despite the examples given, the hedgehog is not often eaten when one considers the numbers available, both living and killed on our roadways. Any other mammal remains that occurred in fox guts or droppings I took to be carrion, including in this category species such as pig, badger and sheep.

Fallow deer make occasional visits to this part of Gloucestershire but I did not find any deer remains during the study period. In Scotland, and probably on Exmoor and in the Lake District, deer carrion may form a significant part of the local foxes' diet, particularly in the winter months. It is said that foxes do occasionally kill weak roe deer and also take the fawns, if available.

The fox is no pig killer, although a local farmer claims that some of his piglets are taken and I cannot really prove he is wrong. This is due to my finding piglet trotters, together with bread, rat remains and fowl feathers, in the stomach of a vixen which was shot not far from his farm. The combination of food stuffs and the knowledge that all these are available from local farm compost heaps, inclines me to believe that on this occasion the vixen was innocent of slaughter and merely a scavenger.

In the summer of 1965 I found a dead fox in Three Oaks Pit. The animal had been dead for a week or so when I found it, yet when I visited the pit again a week or so later the body had been broken up and the head, which I had come to collect, was nowhere to be seen. The only animal capable of carrying off such a prize was another fox and this, together with the exhumations of fox and badger bodies mentioned in the chapter on Fox Senses, indicates that cannibalism does take place. Lund records a fox in a trap eating two of its own toes and also mentions finding cub fur in the gut of another cub.

As proof that foxes eat dead badgers I can quote the vast quantities of badger hair I once found in a fox dropping collected from a nearby wood which has a large badger population. Furthermore, I once found what was obviously a large piece of badger cub skin in a fox dropping; whether or not the fox killed the badger cub I cannot say, but I think it unlikely.

For an animal that is said to be able to charm birds from trees, the fox's consumption of birds is, on the whole, surprisingly low. In April and May bird remains are very commonly found in cub droppings but the number of occurrences declines very rapidly in June when the adults are only occasionally feeding the cubs. In general, bird remains are most frequently found from January to May, after which they do not form an important part of the fox diet, at least in Gloucestershire.

Bird remains were difficult to identify. As a rule, the fox eats only the quill base and down feathers, leaving at the scene of the meal a pile of sheared-off quill feathers together with the wings—and little else apart from the usual dropping deposited upon the remains.

As the fox is popularly thought to live on domestic poultry a check was kept of any losses from local farms. Unfortunately, my neighbour who had so kindly given me permission to wander at will over his farmland, seemed to be the greatest sufferer. During the three years from 1964 to 1966 he lost four cockerels that had been left in an open pig-sty, the wall of which the fox climbed, and three ducks living on the farm pond were attacked. One was killed, taken away and eaten in the adjacent orchard, another died the following day, presumably from injuries received, and the sole survivor was to die, and disappear without more than a feather's trace, on a later occasion. During this latter incident a full-grown goose was beheaded and although the body was salvaged, plucked the same night (or rather early morning) and later made a tasty meal for the family and friends, the head was never discovered. Other losses were reported to me and although at the time they seemed great, when taken over the years they are remarkably low; and if care had been taken to shut up the animals they would have been lower still.

Although the stomach acids would be expected to dissolve bird eggshells this does not always appear to be the case, as on a number of occasions I found complete pieces of shell which could be further broken up with forceps.

Pigeon shoots, during which crows are also sometimes felled and wounded and pheasants and partridges limp away to die unseen, probably provide the fox with many easy meals. I have twice re-covered lead shot from droppings that also contained feathers. Even farm-gibbets of crows are removed by the local foxes, who seem to rely heavily on man-provided, rather than fairly captured, winged prey.

At Kent's Green in 1966, bird remains were commonly found around the dens, either at an entrance or in an adjacent play area in long grass. Species found were blackbird, rook, wood-pigeon and domestic fowl. The buff-tipped vixen I watched in May of that year carrying a blackbird to the cubs at Clewes' Pond Earth was the only occasion I saw an adult fox actually carrying food to cubs, despite numerous observations of vixens visiting cubs at their earths.

The occurrence of blackbird remains in fox droppings is reflected by work done on fox diet in the Crimea, where passerines were found to make up 81 per cent of the occurrences, the blackbird being the most prevalent single species at 2·9 per cent. The same is also true in Norway. One wonders if there is any correlation between the numbers of blackbirds in our hedges, particularly in fruit-growing areas such as Gloucestershire, and their availability to the fox. Certainly I have often seen blackbirds run along the base of a hedge instead of immediately taking flight when I have disturbed them. Sometimes I have thought it was a small mammal scurrying about in the leaf debris at the hedge base, only to find, or rather hear, that the maker of these noises was a blackbird. So it may be that the blackbird crosses the fox's path very frequently, and the habit I have described may increase its vulnerability to the fox.

On fox trails I have found the remains of blackbird, wood-pigeon, rook, moorhen, tawny owl and pheasant, though predation on game birds in the area seems to be very slight, despite the availability of partridges as well as pheasants. Middleton (1957), however, found that foxes were the biggest single predator on pheasants. Conversely, during the last war when gamekeepers were almost non-existent, the numbers of wild pheasants increased. American work, involving the following of over a thousand miles of red-fox trail in grouse country, showed very little predation by the fox on the birds there (Schofield, 1960).

When a fox does attack a sitting pheasant, Middleton claims that the adult bird is killed on the spot, the eggs taken away and some possibly buried, but that the nest itself is little disturbed. In 1965 I found a clutch of partridge eggs near Kent's Green Farm, but here each egg had been broken and the contents consumed, presumably by a rat or a grey squirrel since the nest was much disturbed and broken shells littered the surrounding grass. The following year I found a similar clutch in the same place but this time the eggs vanished without trace. There was no disturbance of the nest and so, on Middleton's views, we must suspect fox predation.

We have already seen that foxes do bury eggs and return to collect them some weeks later, but I doubt whether they are systematic hunters of nests as is sometimes implied. Rather the fox takes advantage of any that happen to occur in its path, without consciously and actively hunting for them.

Birds appear to be most important to the foxes in this country during the spring, when their remains occur very commonly in both adult and cub droppings. These have certain characteristic features: an intense smell and a tendency to bleach and become rock hard after some weeks' exposure to the atmoshpere. Incidentally, the habit of both cub and adult foxes to defecate on the remains of prey is particularly marked on bird remains.

Insects occur very frequently in the diet and are important items of food if considered in terms of percentage occurrence, though the actual volume of insect remains in droppings, and hence in diet, is rarely large. The greatest volume of insect remains I ever found was in a dropping collected in September 1964, which contained a large number of hoverfly larvae skins. These larvae had previously been reported from a fox stomach by Lever (1957). The dropping I collected came from a region of beechwoods in the Cotswolds. Temporary pools of fresh water collect between the exposed roots of many of these trees and it is known that hoverflies lay their eggs in this sort of situation. Presumably, when quenching its thirst from one such pool, the fox inadvertently consumed the hoverfly larvae.

The bulk of the insect remains I found consisted of beetle remains, particularly the elytra, legs and antennae of the genus *Carabus*, but identification of insect remains was seldom attempted beyond family. In the Crimea, insects have been found to make up 49·7 per cent occurrence in the local foxes' diet and, of these, 28·6 per cent were remains of the family *Carabidae*.

Caterpillar skins were sometimes found in fair numbers, particularly empty skins of *Noctuidae* larvae, and this compares well with Neal's findings of similar larvae in badger stomach contents. These larvae are found in grass root systems and are presumably available to the fox when voleing in permanent grassland. Grasshoppers were numerous in the Kent's Green area, yet I only once found the remains of this insect which I would have expected to be of some importance to the fox, considered solely in terms of availability.

A decline in the percentage occurrence of insects in the fox diet in the autumn of 1965 probably correlates with the low beetle population at that time, possibly because of the exceptionally dry summer of 1964. Large numbers of beetles are to be expected in a basically nocturnally-feeding animal such as the fox. If a torch is suddenly switched on whilst one is walking along a rough track, it is surprising just how many ground beetles will walk into the torch beam within a few seconds. It is not, therefore, surprising that both the badger and the fox, who often use well-worn tracks, will pick up in transit a large number of these insects. No hunting and little effort other than a quick snap will be required of the predator during the summer months, though beetles will, of course, be very hard to come by in winter.

For a carnivorous animal, bears excepted, the fox seems to consume a very large quantity of fruit and other vegetation, and this, to me, was the most surprising result of my years of fox-diet study. Passing reference is made in many books and papers to vegetation in the fox diet, but its importance is never stressed, and it is even stated that much of the vegetation found in fox stomachs and droppings has been consumed accidentally along with some more important food item. This may well be so on occasions, but I am convinced that in fruit-growing areas of England at least, fruit is of major importance to the local foxes as part of their staple diet. There is evidence, too, of this in reports from both North America and Europe. It might be thought that, in this country, fruit will only be available for a short time each year, but if one ferrets around in long grass in orchards during winter and even early spring, old mummified fruit will still be found. As I have proved by scat analysis, the fruit, albeit in a decayed and seemingly unappetising state, is still eaten by the fox, despite the availability of what we might consider more nutritious food, and worthier of a carnivore.

In lowland Gloucestershire, where there is much fruit growing, the potential food supply for the fox is relatively great, particularly as regards pears and apples. It is some years now since there was a large enough plum crop for it to figure significantly in the fox diet. Much of the local fruit is harvested for cider and perry manufacture, and the old large trees, particularly pear, are often shaken to dislodge the ripe fruit. Much of this falls into the long grass around the trees where it is lost to man but provides an open larder for the fox and other animals. This reservoir of fruit forms an important food supply for most of the winter months.

A further supply of apples is also available to the fox during the winter as a result of the local practice of dumping surplus fruit into old marl pits or near the edges of orchards. Three such dumps occurred in my study area and are marked on Fig 2. Fox scent was often recognised near these dumps, particularly in January 1966 at the pit near Clewes' Farm. One evening that month, when I was sitting waiting for the 'wo-wo' fox to start its evening barkings, I became aware of the intense fox smell beneath my feet and saw by the light of my torch a number of fresh scats on a pile of rotting apples. A few minutes after I switched off my torch I heard footsteps approaching along the roadway close by and, although I was unable to see the animal making towards the pit, I was convinced it was the local fox coming for its evening dessert. It must have picked up my scent despite the strong cider haze around the pit and decided that fruit was not on the menu that night, for it galloped off down the road the way it had come.

Blackberry pips did not occur in fox scats from Kent's Green despite the abundant availability of the fruit. Poor plum crops each year prevented this fruit making a greater contribution to the fox diet but on the few occasions I did find plum stones, they occurred in large numbers, indicating that foxes relish this fruit. A less expected find was a large quantity of yew berries in droppings of both fox and badger at Woodchester Park on the Cotswolds, near Stroud. The seed always came through the animal's gut whole, together with the red aril, the two together giving a very characteristic appearance to the resultant scat.

In an attempt to trace the movements of the local foxes, I introduced small pieces of metal, inscribed with a number and date, into apples and pears which I then placed at strategic positions on fox highways in the hope that the foxes would eat the fruit, plus metal, and that the latter would turn up at some later date inside a scat. I tried the experiment for a number of weeks and even used cubes of ox heart as bait, but I only recovered one metal tag and that from a scat collected on the far side of a field hedge only a few feet from where I had placed it in the bait. But even though I gained very little information from this technique, I still think it worth further investigation and suggest that it could prove a useful aid in determining fox ranges.

Fruit was found in scats during most months of the year, except between January and May 1964 and March and May 1965. I was able to watch fox cubs eating fruit in the orchard near Upper Allisons in September 1964. Two foxes from that year's litter were eating pears, while not far away a brown hare appeared to be doing likewise. The cubs apparently disregarded the hare and their indifference was mutual for, although obviously aware of the foxes, the hare continued eating only a few yards away.

Lever records grass as being the only plant remain of importance in his study of British fox diet, but does also record apple, pear, sloe, cherry and blackberry. In my study area, fruit would seem to be of great importance to the local foxes, particularly in the autumn when the young cubs are feeding themselves. It may well be, indeed, that the presence of a good fruit supply is instrumental in reducing cub mortality.

Other plant remains were often found and sometimes formed a significant part of scats. Of these, grass was of major importance and though some of it was no doubt taken accidentally while the fox was catching small rodents, the bulk of the grass remains suggests that much was taken deliberately. In February 1964, grass leaves formed a high percentage of the total scat content, but I found no correlation between occurrence of grass and the remains of field voles. Rather, I found that when fruit is scarce grass appears frequently. An odd find was that of corn, particularly wheat seeds with husk, in scats collected during the late summer and this formed 100 per cent of two scats I found in July 1964. I also found sedge leaves, clover, moss and acorns, but all were of minor importance.

Losses of sheep, particularly in spring, are usually regarded as being caused by fox predation. Farmers claim to lose not only lambs but grown sheep on occasions and I have heard it said that, when a ewe has twins, the fox is supposed to try to draw the mother away from one of the lambs 'knowing full well that she cannot look after two'. The fox is then said to pounce upon the isolated lamb. Admittedly, my experience of sheep is not great but a number of farming friends tell me they often have trouble in getting ewes to feed twins, one lamb often being rejected. This may be nature's way of ensuring that, if the ewe has only enough milk for one lamb, both will not die. The neglected lamb would soon die under natural conditions and it is this dead or very weak animal, rather than the healthy one which, I suggest, is taken by the fox. For this the fox requires no 'cunning'— merely patience; it is all too easy to blame the fox rather than the farming methods. Losses of lambs are reported most frequently in hill-farming areas, but just how many of the dead lambs found outside earths have actually been killed by foxes is a point to be established before we condemn the animal.

Unfortunately the fox suffers probably more than any other British mammal through a misunderstanding of its way of life. Popular misconceptions about the fox are so deeply ingrained that people find it difficult to be objective when talking or writing about them. A fox, one suspects, is often a useful excuse to cover up inefficiency. How many stillborn lambs, one wonders, could be saved by better management of the ewes? And if the fox carries off the bodies he is a very convenient scapegoat to be accused of the slaughter. Foxes may occasionally kill lambs but, if they do, I suspect the lambs are sickly or very weak.

In the winter of 1965 I helped a local farmer with his lambing and was staggered by the losses of new-born lambs in a sudden and unexpected spell of bitter weather. The combination of a biting wind and an open field, even in lowland Gloucestershire, meant that nine lambs died soon after birth. The dead lambs, in this case, were buried in an old well but had they remained in the field overnight, the fox would no doubt have helped itself and left the evidence outside its earth. The following summer one of the surviving lambs suddenly developed a mysterious illness that brought its death within a few days—something which might not have been noticed in a larger flock on hilly ground until a fox had removed the body and again left evidence for man to condemn him as the killer. Evidence of foxes actually having been seen to kill lambs and sheep is almost non-existent—extraordinary indeed when one considers the numbers of lambs that foxes are supposed to kill each year.

Brian Vesey-Fitzgerald says that, in lowland country, the dog is a more serious menace to sheep than the fox. He quotes Home Office figures over fourteen years which showed that 69,573 sheep were reported to have been killed by dogs, an average of nearly 5,000 per year, over and above a yearly total of about 4,000 sheep which had been injured. The Ministry of Agriculture does not, it seems, keep records of the number of sheep and lambs killed by the fox—such information as is available is thought to be too unreliable.

Two surveys were, however, carried out by the Welsh Department of the Ministry of Agriculture in 1962, covering farms in part of North Cardiganshire and North Pembrokeshire. They showed that whereas some farmers never, or rarely suffered loss, others did so frequently, and this seems to me to be highly significant. Although the sample was small the losses, which varied on different farms from 0·3 per cent to 3·3 per cent, suggest, as Vesey-Fitzgerald points out, that more money is spent on killing foxes than the lambs supposed to be lost to them are worth.

Foxes, we know, will eat bloodstained wool clipped from the crutch of a ewe and thrown away by the farmer, so that the mere presence of sheep wool in fox stomachs is no proof of fox killing sheep. I have found sheep wool in some fox scats and in one stomach, but in each case I suspect it was derived from carrion. Even after myxomatosis had killed off most of the rabbit population, only five counties in England, and one in Wales, reported an increase in lamb or sheep killing by foxes; one even reported a decrease.

Thus the fox would seem to be condemned by circumstantial evidence mainly arising from its activities as a scavenger. An objective outlook is hardly to be expected when economic factors, such as stock losses to predators, are involved, and we do know that foxes will at times, and given the opportunity, kill many species of domestic animal. But how often do they do this, and just how important is the effect of fox predation on livestock? Surprisingly few scientific studies have been carried out on the relative proportions of each type of food item in a fox's diet, with the result that casual observations, particularly those made at earths, have led to the conclusion that foxes live mainly by killing domestic animals and game. Consequently, all hands seem to be turned against *Vulpes vulpes*.

Yet what do scientifically-based observations on fox predation really show? They show that in Norway, Sweden, the United States and Russia, at least, fox predation has very little effect on the population of game birds and, while losses of domestic animals are often reported, evidence of foxes actually killing the prey whose remains are found outside the earths is very scanty indeed. This, I think, is the crux of the fox problem: just how much of the fox's food is actually killed by the predator and how much is carrion? To find the answer to this problem is more difficult than one might imagine. Unless lead shot is found associated with partridge feathers in a fox's scat or stomach, it is difficult to prove the fox's innocence—or guilt, for that matter.

We have already seen plenty of direct evidence of scavenging but even better proof of this habit can be obtained by snow tracking. If a fox snow trail is followed, one gains much information about where the fox obtained its food and how much of it was carrion. Scrapes dug in the fox's search for voles under the snow are often seen, as is evidence of foxes attempting to catch larger living prey. If I can generalise from the studies of snow trails undertaken in North America and Scandinavia, it appears that the fox seldom catches fast-moving or potentially fast-moving prey. Most of the game birds the fox eats have either died natural deaths due to cold or have flown into high-tension cables—a very common source of carrion. Additionally, there are the birds injured by man and other predators. During twenty-five miles of following fox trails in Wisconsin, Karpuleon (1958) found that during two winters the foxes killed nine rabbits and twenty-five small mammals, and had on seven occasions visited the carrion of larger animals. No hares were eaten, even though they were more numerous in the area than rabbits, nor had the foxes caught any game birds. In Michigan, over a four-year period, an investigator (Schofield) covered 1,109 miles of fox tracks. The most important food item was deer carrion, followed by small mammals. The only game animals found to have been killed by the local foxes were five cotton-tail rabbits, two bob-white quail and one snowshoe hare. Hares are seldom found in the fox diet in any part of the range of the red fox.

The effort of killing living prey is, it seems, seldom necessary but when the occasion arises, as it might, for example, in spring, when young cubs are to be fed, the fox will, as we know, kill. From my own observations and those of others who have studied fox diet, we know that the quantity of, for instance, poultry taken over a whole year is very small indeed and this seems to apply equally to other domestic animals and game.

If foxes really were keeping the numbers of game birds down, one would expect a substantial increase if the fox population were to be severely reduced or even locally exterminated. Yet there is no such increase it seems, and in one study (Scott, 1950) in Iowa, where the local foxes were said to be responsible for the decline in numbers of *Colineus sp*, an investigation of 472 stomachs from captured foxes showed that only one had remains of the bird in question. Such efforts at destruction apparently prove both expensive and valueless, for the fox numbers soon build up again and there is no increase in the amount of game bagged while they are doing so.

In North Missouri in 1951, there was an estimated fox population of twelve to twenty per square mile, and yet the author of a paper describing this could still report that the effect of fox predation upon game animals during his five years' study was minor.

THE DIET OF THE CUBS

Between 1964–6 I was able to collect a number of cub scats from earths, in most cases after the cubs had left. On one occasion, as I have recounted, I did collect from Big Earth Pit while cubs were present and watched my activities but there was no subsequent removal of cubs from the earth even though my scent must have been liberally distributed about the precincts. Probably, occasional collecting like this will not lead to abandonment of earths the following night, as seems to be widely assumed; my presence must have been noticed many times at and around earths, yet no movement of cubs took place immediately afterwards. Or perhaps the local foxes have become so used to my particular scent that they do not react violently to it; just as deer are said to become used to the scent of foresters' boots.

Cub scats were sometimes found inside the earth in the immediate surroundings, or in the play areas where I often collected them from prey remains. In March, no cub droppings were found; they first appeared when the cubs came above ground in April and were then collected at the earths until the middle of May. After that, all the scats came from the play areas and lying-up places under hedges. The majority of the scats were collected in May, the time when the cubs were most active in and around the earth.

The diagram at Fig 14 shows that at first, as one would expect, the cub diet consists largely of food items brought by the adults—I suspect by the vixen in most cases (Plate 9b). In April we would expect and do, in fact, find, that birds and mammals are the major items in the cubs' diet. Milk can also be found in cub stomachs and there seems to be some evidence for the suggestion that the adult fox regurgitates food to the cubs. In May, items the cubs can obtain by their own devices become much more important, mainly worms, insects, grass and trash. Considerable amounts of sand are often found in scats after the cubs have been eating worms and, unless microscopic examination of the sand is made to discover chaetae of worms, the sand is likely to be included under the heading of 'trash taken accidentally', which it most certainly is not in most cases I investigated. Cubs do eat a large amount of grass, much of it probably taken accidentally as they are not very efficient at separating the large number of insects they consume from the attendant grass blades. By June, the proportion of adult-provided food is low compared with that obtained by the cubs themselves, and this marks the beginning of cub independence from the adults.

Many of the sixty-five droppings I found in October 1964 were, I suspect, from the local cubs and the proportion of fruit content was large. Survival of a large litter in the late summer and early autumn may, I think, be largely dependent on a good local fruit crop, as fox

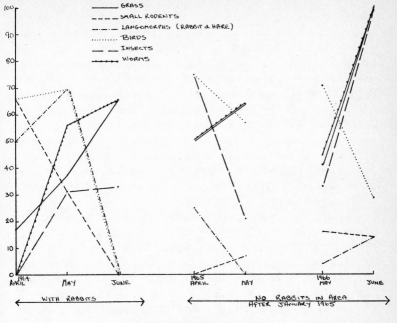

14. Cub diet in spring and early summer

population is at its highest at this time of the year and competition for available food presumably most intense. In Norway, the fox cubs have most vegetation in their diet in July and September which, if one again allows for difference of latitude and the later birth dates of the cubs, would agree with my results from Gloucestershire.

The finding of milk in fox cubs which had been destroyed suggests that the vixen suckles her young for two or three weeks before she brings them solid food. They are then rapidly weaned and, at Kent's Green, the cubs are independent by the end of June.

As we have seen, the fox will eat, with a few notable exceptions, whatever is available to it; available, that is, in the sense that the food item, plant or animal, is present in the home range and also vulnerable. An animal or plant may be present in abundance in a particular area and yet never or only rarely turn up in the local fox

121

diet. Animals which are available and yet not often vulnerable are woodmice, rats, squirrels, hares and bank voles. All are common and reasons must be found for their relative safety from foxes. Squirrels are hard to catch for a terrestrial predator and probably only the stray unfortunate caught in open ground is captured; apart from which the activity times of fox and squirrel do not overlap much for most of the year. Habitat preferences may largely take the bank vole and woodmouse out of the foxes' sphere of influence. Both are more characteristic of hedgerow and woodland than of open grassland. The woodmouse is an extremely agile animal and climbs very well indeed, while the bank vole is a dweller in deep, scrubby litter where the fox's mousing techniques cannot be used. The speed of hares may reduce their availability to foxes but what about rats? There does not seem to be an obvious reason for their poor showing as fox food, especially when one considers their supposed vulnerability to fox mimicry!

Insectivores represent some of the notable exceptions to the statement that a fox eats whatever is available. Hedgehogs are eaten, it is true, but not very often considering their abundance; shrews and moles are almost ignored, except the latter during early spring when fox cubs are to be fed. It has been suggested that the smell, and therefore the taste, of small insectivores is repulsive to predators. If so, since cubs seem to eat them when proffered, this would indicate an apparent adult sophistication which the young are not allowed. We know from feeding tests that the fox prefers not to eat insectivores unless hard-pressed, and so availability in this case is not followed by consumption.

Availability of field voles would seem to increase in the autumn and early winter, when populations are probably at their greatest and distribution over their habitat extensive. It is at this time, as we have seen, that fox consumption of voles and mammals in general is at its highest, yet, despite this, the fox in autumn still eats a large amount of fruit and insects. My impression is that the fox, being essentially a lazy animal, eats whatever is most easily procured and collecting fallen fruit in an orchard is much less strenuous and time-consuming than hunting for voles.

If one correlates available food in an area with ease of collection then one can, I believe, predict what foxes in a given area will be eating at different times of the year, remembering their preference for certain species. Availability of small mammals, such as voles, will not

122

only depend upon the animal's habitat preferences, activity pattern and general behaviour, but also upon climatic conditions. In periods of deep snow, the field vole is more protected from fox predation than in a mild, snow-free winter. Similarly, droughts will send earthworms deeper into the ground and so temporarily remove them from the foxes 'potential food' list.

I am thus again forced to the conclusion expressed at the beginning of this chapter, that foxes, even at high densities, have little if any effect on natural populations. The one glaring exception to this conclusion is the previously-mentioned study at Ravenglass, in Cumberland, where foxes accounted for 825 black-headed gulls in 1962, 230 of them in one night; 1,100 young gulls were also killed and eggs were taken and buried one by one at a short distance from the robbed nests.

This, one might say, is surely an example of foxes having a great effect on a natural population, but is it? Sea birds prefer not to build nests on islands frequented by foxes, and could this not be a natural regulator tending to reduce considerably a breeding population of gulls choosing a bad nesting area—bad, that is, from the point of view of safety from predators? Because an area is a nature reserve and we wish to conserve the gull breeding, we control the fox population and thereby allow a large colony to thrive in what is really an artificial environment free from predators. In this sense, the population can no longer be considered a natural one and so does not invalidate my earlier conclusion.

Fox
Society

SOCIAL ORGANISATION

The adult fox is a solitary animal except during the breeding season, and as I have never seen two adults together, I cannot speak from first-hand experience about what happens when they meet. I have heard vocal evidence of encounters between foxes and have sometimes found double trails, either in snow or mud, indicating that two foxes were travelling together, but this is my only direct evidence of social contact.

There are two sources of information which enable us to discover something about fox society. One is from observations by people who have kept captive foxes and studied their activities, and the other is from watching the behaviour of wild foxes coming to bait, as has been done by Vincent in North America. From such observations we do know that foxes, in common with most other mammals, sort themselves out when they meet into a social or pecking order. One animal in an area seems to become dominant over all the others. This animal, or despot as Vincent calls it, may be male or female, although in most cases the top animal seems to be the dog fox. Below the despot are arranged, in order, the various other animals in the vicinity. Once this social scale has been sorted out the animals live in fairly close proximity to one another although probably seldom making direct contact. The pecking order may change as new animals come into the area or old ones die. It is not a long term set-up and is probably established twice a year, in autumn and again in spring, and as we shall see, the position of an animal in the scale may be temporarily changed during the breeding season.

How is this social scale determined in the fox?

The most obvious way would be for the animals to fight for position, and actual physical combat has been observed both in captive and free-living animals. Tembrock (1962) has filmed and analysed the behaviour of two dog foxes during such a conflict. Vincent claims that foxes fight silently, and his and other reports speak of much blood-letting and fur loss during these fights, without, apparently, any great amount of physical harm being done to either party. This violent form of combat is said always to involve the dominant animal in an area, whose mere presence seems to bring about the retreat of the intruder or subordinate animal who is pursued and attacked.

I have found no evidence of this type of combat at Kent's Green, although I have had chases described to me. One chase continued in the observer's view for about a quarter of a mile along an open Cotswold hillside and ended when the trailing fox turned and retraced its steps to a cover that was known to contain a breeding earth. This incident took place in the late afternoon of a January day in good light. Another chase was described to me from the Cotswolds during the same season. A common feature of these chases was the hoarse screaming that accompanied the pursuit.

Other less violent means of determining social rank described by Vincent are rather ritualised performances and do not lead to bloodshed. The antagonists face one another, each places its forepaws on the shoulder of the other, and the animal able to push the other backwards is apparently the winner. This type of combat is accompanied by much wide-mouthed screaming and yelling. (See figure at head of chapter on Music and Movement and Plate 11a.)

Aggressive intent upon the part of the contestants is shown by baring of the teeth, snarling and the erection of neck hairs. After pushing, the animals may separate slightly, lie down a few feet apart and continue the crying and screaming. (See photograph of dog fox in a typical attitude in Plate 11b.) The subordinate animal, it seems, then retreats from the scene with its tail between its legs—a posture very reminiscent of that in a submissive dog.

A third form of combat, again non-violent, is said to be typical of combat between members of opposite sexes. Here there is no physical contact, the foxes simply lie or sit screaming at one another with their muzzles between one and ten inches apart. They may maintain this position for up to fifteen minutes before breaking off the encounter.

What would seem to be a variation of the ritualised fighting that Vincent mentions was an incident described to me by Mr F. Clewes of Kent's Green. At 10 am on 17 January 1966, near Clewes' Farm Earth and close to the spot where I had recorded the 'wo-wo' fox a few days before, he watched two adult foxes performing a high leaping 'dance'. It seems the animals ran in rough circles around one another and frequently leapt into the air, making brief bodily contact during these manœuvres. During this performance also there was much loud screaming. I have seen much the same kind of aggressive play among cubs in the late summer and think it significant that similar behaviour patterns should be shown by adults and cubs, both of which, in my opinion, are establishing their social position by these activities.

Once the social scale has been decided, the animals are normally kept apart by scent and barking, which we may term social spacing mechanisms. When the spacing mechanism breaks down, as at food or during the breeding season, then one of the forms of combat described above will decide the issue again. The temporary change in an animal's social position during the breeding season, when mated animals seem to share the social position of the higher animal, usually means the upgrading of the female, although the reverse can apply if the vixen is top animal in the area.

It is known that in weasels there may be a temporary change in social position when the normally subordinate female becomes pregnant and drives off the male. The position is reversed when the young grow up or are accidentally killed. This may, I think, also happen in the case of the vixen driving off the dog fox after she becomes pregnant. I have some vocal evidence that this might take place, for on a number of occasion I have heard screaming in March before the cubs are born. This rejection of the male may, of course, take place if the vixen is the dominant animal temporarily subordinating herself tō a dog fox during the rut, only to reassert her social position when the rut ceases.

It appears from Vincent's observations that strong social ties are sometimes built up between a dog fox and a vixen, although the duration of this association is not known. In one instance a vixen at first attacked and defeated a newly-arrived dog fox, but on a second encounter the tables were reversed; subsequently, the vixen made a number of passes at the dog until a bond of some sort was established —we are not told, however, if the animals mated. Another, to me, very important observation was made during the same study when a dog fox mated with a new vixen, either after his previous mate died or because the union had been terminated at the close of the previous breeding season.

This record does cast great doubt on the reputed faithfulness of dog foxes who, some authors claim, mate for life and if the partner is killed will not take another vixen. This theory has never been substantiated for free-living foxes but is based, it seems, on the difficulty experienced in trying to mate silver fox males polygamously. But this can be achieved if the dogs are allowed to settle down for a while with different vixens.

It is very dangerous, however, to generalise from captive animal behaviour taking place under artificial conditions, and to expect a similar type of behaviour in the wild. Experiments in breeding cats in captivity show that a male, if introduced into a strange cage with a female who is on heat and receptive, will not mate with her until he has established a territorial claim to the cage. After this, the male cat will mate with any female that happens to be present in his territory. We probably have a similar blockage to breeding in captive foxes who, under natural conditions, may be decidedly polygamous.

Social contact would seem, therefore, to be aimed at determining a social gradation with neither sex, nor length of residence in a particular area, alone determining relative position, although this latter factor may on occasions give the resident a slight advantage. This social organisation seems to be set up in autumn and maintained until after the breeding season. After this, I suspect that the organisation breaks down, as does the temporary relationship between dog and vixen or vixens, and is only slowly built up again the following winter, it being fortuitous if a couple that mated one year mate again.

Social structure is maintained by aggressive activities, mainly vocal and olfactory, the vocal mechanism being the screaming and also the dog foxes' 'wo-wo' type bark in the winter months while the vixens are on heat; the olfactory being the scenting and dropping behaviour already described.

Young animals probably start their first season well down the social scale but the highest cub in the adult society will, as far as I am concerned, be the animal that played the hardest and was the most adventurous during the time the cubs lived together after losing their dependence on the vixen for food.

CUB SOCIETY

Play

When we apply this word 'play' to animals' activities, we immediately run into difficulties in defining just what activities to include. In carnivores, play activities are said to be particularly characteristic and well developed in the young, but also to take place in the adult. Under the heading 'play' are such activities as chasing, leaping, mock fights and pouncing on inanimate objects or on other members of the litter. These movements may or may not be accompanied by vocal activity in the form of squealing, growling or barking.

What is the function of play, if it has one? A number of theories have been suggested, including getting rid of surplus energy, practising movements that will be later used to capture prey, and getting to know the environment. None of these is considered to be a complete explanation in itself. Although they may give part of the answer, they do not cover play as a general activity in all animals of all ages, which I think a general theory must do.

After watching fox cubs performing their characteristic play movements, I have come to the conclusion they are not non-directed movements in the sense that they appear to have little immediate purpose. Rather do I regard them as directed activities, in that they have a goal, and so 'play', with its human connotations, is not an appropriate word to use. I suggest that the goal of play is the establishment of a social hierarchy or 'pecking order' among young animals; we readily recognise such a social rank in adult animals, particularly the herd species. In these, the establishment of a pecking order leads to tolerably good relationships between the individual members of a group, each of which has its dominant and subordinate animals.

A pecking order can be a straightforward chain: A pecks B, B pecks C and so on; or it can be a more complicated, even triangular relationship, such as A pecks B, B pecks C but the latter is dominant to A. The linear system seems to be the most common order. There is also a gradation between the way in which A asserts its dominance over B, compared with that of B over C. Animals lower down the social order tend to be more aggressive towards those below them, whereas the violence done to a subordinate seems to decrease in intensity as the social ladder is climbed; this has been found to hold true for monkeys and fowl. In a fox litter it is also, I think, the lower-ranking, weaker animals which seem to be subject to the worst treatment, although the presence of the dominant animal in a litter may inhibit the violence when subordinate animals 'play' with one another. In this way the top animal may protect the weaker member of a litter and this could lead to the establishment of a bond between top and bottom animal.

Play in a litter of fox cubs is at first rather mild and consists mainly of individual play with inanimate objects, such as pieces of wood or bits of earth, with an occasional brief fight, usually between two cubs one of whom usually ends up astride the other, who lies on its back. The exchanges are brief and the cubs return to their solitary activities very soon. Frequently, I have seen only one cub at an earth although I have known that a litter has been present. In June, there is the beginning of vocal activity accompanying the cubs' play. This takes place just after dark and sounds very much like cats fighting but can be broken down into two main sounds, screaming and 'tch, tch'ing'.

In July and August the play at dusk is very hectic and vocal, with much screaming and 'tch'ing' accompanying the chases and stiff-legged pounces. On one occasion in August 1966 I heard the fighting noise from the hedge next to Savage's Pond Earth and a few seconds after it had subsided a cub appeared at the edge of the field. After looking around for a few seconds it lay down and remained in that position for about fifteen minutes as darkness fell. It then stood up and made its way along the edge of the field and out of sight. On another occasion I watched a cub sleep, or at least rest, for about ten minutes outside the earth.

The play appears gradually to become more and more aggressive in its nature and, by the time it is accompanied by vocal elements, to be aggressive in intent. The two cubs I saw sleeping briefly away from the other cubs may have been forcibly-ejected, middle-ranking animals, or at least may have removed themselves for a little peace from constant intimidation.

Whereas in social animals aggressive play probably leads to the establishment of a junior pecking order which allows the animals to live in close proximity to one another, the aggressive play in fox cubs and other predators, such as polecats and weasels, probably leads to the break-up of the family and so to the typical solitary existence of the adult. The animals that remain together longest in a fox litter may be, as I have suggested, from opposite ends of the social scale, and probably of opposite sexes.

The beginning of vocal activity in the fox cubs' play sessions in summer seems to me to mark the end of what I call social aggressive play, which ceases before the underdog is physically harmed. Screaming in cubs marks, I think, the onset of aggressive play with intent to intimidate and physically subordinate the 'victim' of the play activity. Probably the change from juvenile to adolescence in the cubs as the sex organs develop, provides the physiological stimulus for the change in intensity and purpose of the play. The beginning of sexual maturity would seem to me to be associated with the increase in the vocal content of the play, that is the screaming. I wonder if any teenage human analogy is permissible here?

Play, then, in very young foxes is almost non-vocal and the noises produced are not screamings. At this stage, probably because of their immaturity, the animals seldom hurt one another but as the sex organs develop, so does the vocal element in the play and with it the aggressive intention, until finally the cubs become solitary.

True aggression is not shown by adults towards cubs even when the latter attempt to intimidate their elders during the visits of vixens to their cubs. As the cubs mature, however, the adult seems to lose its inhibitions about hurting the cubs. The adult's aggressive intentions probably increase on each encounter with a growing cub until the latter is forcibly expelled from the vixen's area in late summer.

TERRITORY

In 1964 I found three litters of fox cubs within a few hundred yards of one another; a year later only one litter was found in the same area and, in 1966, two. I was able to watch the vixens that produced the latter families—'Buff Tip' at Clewes' Pond Earth and 'White Tip' at Grange Earth. Both vixens, I knew, hunted over the same trails for I had followed their movements on a number of sunny, windy days in the spring and summer.

Two vixens—three on occasions—in one small 'neck of the woods'. What about their relationship with one another, if any? How did their respective males—two, three, perhaps more—behave themselves socially? Or was it just one dog with a number of vixens? My conclusions as to the answers to these questions have been suggested by my own field observations and reliable reports from other observers, but though the theory I have produced fits all the evidence I have accumulated, this is not to say that it is correct. At least, however, it is a working basis which later and more detailed observations may confirm or reject.

Territory implies an area of land that is actively defended by an animal and within which the resident individual is paramount, even when faced by a potentially stronger member of its species. In my consideration of the question of fox territory, I started with the basic assumption that the fox is a territorial animal; that is one that stakes out by various means a definite area of land. This territory has clearly fixed boundaries which the resident animal regularly patrols and defends against all comers.

Various questions arose from this assumption. Did dog foxes and vixens establish separate territories, or did only the dog fox claim an area of land? When and how did the markings of the territory boundaries take place? Were territories of a semi-permanent nature and only taken over by a new owner when the resident animal died or was defeated in battle? How big are these territories if they exist?

I cannot claim to have completely answered the questions posed but I have tried, on the basis of my field evidence, to produce a territorial theory which fits in with my observations. One point is clear—both dog foxes and vixens mark various points in their environment by means of droppings, scent and urine. I think that dog foxes establish a territory, while vixens establish their social rank by the various scenting activities mentioned. I will, therefore, deal with each sex separately.

Dog-Fox Territory

I distinguish here between territory which is a temporarily defended area of small dimensions, and the home range which I define as the area in which the fox lives after the rut. Dog foxes, I believe, establish and maintain their territories by both barking and scenting.

Winter Barks

In December, a number of foxes could often be heard barking together in a fairly small area and it was then that I was able to distinguish between the voices; by going out to listen nearly every evening I soon became vocally familiar with the different foxes making them. It occurred to me that it should be possible to map out roughly the area over which a particular fox barked, if indeed there was a constant pattern about such things. For over a month, therefore, I went out whenever possible and followed the barking foxes as they moved along, for I soon found that a fox seldom barked from one spot twice but barks whilst moving. Instead of following the foxes directly (a technique I tried but soon gave up), I either walked, cycled or drove about the lanes and plotted on a map the position of each barking fox every time I heard it. A pattern of barking did emerge and I found that the three Kent's Green barking foxes stayed consistently in a certain area of country, at least during the barking sessions. On occasions I could hear all three barking at each other in a small area. On one occasion I was listening to the 'wo-wo' fox as it moved along Woodman's orchard, when I became aware of the 'wo-wo-wo-wo' fox barking in the distance towards Taynton Church. The 'wo-wo' fox swung off its usual barking trail and because it continued to bark, as did the other fox, I was able to hear the two foxes closing the gap between them until the calls ceased. What happened then I do not know.

The barking area of the 'wo-wo' fox became best known to me and I was able to follow its progress by ear during January 1966. It seemed to centre its activities at Clewes' Farm, where there was an earth in the steep bank of a marl pit which had a pond in the bottom. I have previously described my attempts to make a tape recording of this fox's barking, which usually started the moment the farm milking machine was switched on in the evening.

This 'wo-wo' type of barking, which is mainly to be heard in winter and then for a few weeks only, seems to be associated with the period during which the vixens are on heat. I do not think this call is a contact bark, at least in winter, for there has not been any vocal evidence of so-called answering barks from foxes travelling together along parallel tracks; in fact, as I have indicated, the barks are aggressive rather than social in function, the animals barking at rather than to one another. The foxes had very definite routes to which they kept during the barking and I think they were dog foxes barking out their territory and warning off would-be intruders. I also think it significant that the barking and the heat period of the vixen both last approximately three weeks and that these events seem to coincide. I suggest that the dog fox is at his most aggressive during the vixen's heat period and that barking is an expression of this attitude towards other males and may also help to stimulate the female to mate.

I have not, of course, been able completely to define the dog-fox territories, but only to distinguish by sign reading some of the area in which I think fox territories meet. In the section on droppings, I have said that the distribution of these varies from week to week and that first one and then another has a concentration of sign. From this I assume that the fox marks its boundaries in this way until the whole perimeter is defined.

Based on the barking evidence, the dog-fox's territory is not of great extent and seems to be oval rather than circular, the greatest diameter being less than a mile and the smallest half a mile. This would apply to the 'wo-wo' fox, at least.

The home range size of two adult males, captured and fitted with small radio transmitters in the United States, was found to be 910 and 1,040 acres. The size of the territory is probably less than the home range, and both may well depend upon population density and food supply in any particular area.

Scent Marking

We know that many mammals mark or rub scent from body glands on to objects of importance in their environment, such as a tree, gate-post, pile of stones or a clump of grass. This behaviour, together with urination on selected objects, is very well developed in the *Canidae*.

The fox certainly uses urine and sub-caudal gland secretions to mark its surroundings. On two occasions only have I been able to watch a fox actually scenting by using sub-caudal gland secretion, and possibly urine as well. These incidents took place on 13 and 14 September 1965 while I was sitting in a tree overlooking Savage's orchard, where many trails could be seen in the long grass. At 8.20 on the evening of the 13th, when it was dusk, there was a rustling in the grass and I trained my binoculars in the direction of the disturbance. I was able to make out fairly clearly what appeared to be a large fox with a conspicuous white tip to its tail. The animal was walking rather slowly and sedately, picking its feet up well and its brush was arched behind it (see photograph of dog foxes (Plate 7b)). The base of a pear tree was the first object to be treated by the fox, which placed its rear against the trunk and rubbed violently, its tail lashing from side to side. Movements of the fox, and the tail in particular, could easily be followed from the almost luminous white tip. The rubbing took about twenty seconds after which the performance, including the stiff walk, was repeated at another nearby tree. Next to receive attention was a small clump of dead, woody vegetation rising about a foot above the general grass level. The whole clump waved violently from side to side as the fox rubbed against it in a very purposeful manner. Nor was grass neglected, the fox seeming to roll in this after rubbing its anal region vigorously on the flattened area. The whole process was watched for about five minutes, during which three trees, one bush and three areas of grass were scented. The following evening the fox again began to scent in the orchard but seemed to detect my presence and made off before it came near me.

All this activity was quite deliberate and had associated with it a special walk and tail posture. I was unable to determine the sex of the animal, but I think it of interest that the performance, with its well-defined body postures, took place in the absence of any other fox. Possibly this behaviour is also used to display to another fox but has become so ritualised that the fox still goes through all the motions even in the absence of a visual stimulus. Or perhaps the stimulus in this case was an olfactory one.

Both sexes use urine for marking purposes and have special body postures associated with this activity which enable us to distinguish between scent marking and simple elimination of urine or faeces. Klineman (1966) gives three characteristics of scent-marking behaviour. The animal must be attracted to and take up a position near a specific object or to the source of a smell. The stimulus which brings about the movement must either be new objects or well-known landmarks on which it has previously deposited scent, and thirdly, the pattern must be repeated frequently when the animal is subject to the same stimulus.

I have several times observed urination in the fox without the event being particularly concerned with scenting and it is then possible to get a clue as to the sex of a fox by noticing the posture adopted. The vixen generally squats down into nearly a sitting position with the tail held parallel to the ground. A similar position is sometimes adopted by the dog fox but it does not lower its hindquarters so much. Dog foxes also adopt various other postures depending upon the plane of the surface to be anointed. A dog-like hind leg lift is used against a vertical surface. When directing urine on to the ground, the fox either stands with its legs slightly spread or raises and bends one hind leg under its body. A squatting position has been observed in dog foxes marking with urine. Female foxes when marking, either squat or squat and raise one hind leg under the body.

The frequency with which a fox urinates seems to depend upon the season, urine marking being at its greatest in the winter months during the rut. Snow trails, too, as already mentioned, often show evidence of this activity. The rôle of faeces in marking is less well-established fox behaviour, though my field evidence convinces me that foxes do use faeces for marking purposes.

To return to Klineman's criteria for marking; I have evidence to show that faeces are deposited on specific objects both new and old, as is required to comply with the criteria. For example, the salt block I previously mentioned finding well decorated with scats in January 1965 was ringed by fox footprints and I collected five separate scats which must have been produced either by a number of foxes using the same site, or one fox returning regularly to the same point to defecate. A similar example is mentioned by Scott in the United States; he found a dead dog which had been decorated with fox scats in the same way as had my salt lick. Earlier references have also been made to the fox's habit of leaving a scat on food remains and new objects in its environment.

In July 1964, and again in September of that year, I found large numbers of fox scats on man-made roadways. Both the paths so treated were foresters' roadways and for a week or so fresh scats were deposited on them. This habit seems to be similar to that observed by Lockie in pine martens.

Finally, in January 1965 and 1966 I found collections of scats at certain points on the rutting trails, particularly near the water jumps. The position of fox scats in hedge gaps in January of each year, and the way in which the location of scat concentrations varied from week to week, convinced me, with the other observations mentioned, that the fox does use defecation as a means of marking, particularly during the rutting period. This seems to be territorial marking and to last only during the rut, for at other times of the year scats appear to be distributed more or less at random along trails or in open places.

I have said a territory is an area that is actively defended, but barking and scent-marking activities seem hardly to constitute active defence. The marking seems to be psychological warfare, for a strange animal entering a well-marked territory is probably on the defensive and likely to come off second best in any encounter with the resident animal. That these encounters rarely take place is, I believe, because the scenting technique is so effective in keeping strangers away. When foxes do meet, however, there follows a screaming match or a mock fight involving much high leaping accompanied by cat-like screaming. Physical damage to either participant must be very rare and the resident fox that knows the area well will usually be the victor in this ritualised type of combat.

The diagram at Fig 15 illustrates my belief that a dog fox's territory may contain one or several vixens and that his boundaries are well defined. The dog fox probably begins to establish his claim to a

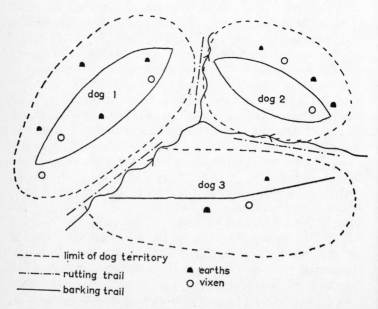

15. Diagram of suggested disposition of dog-fox territories in winter

territory in late autumn when, as a result of the high mortality among vixens in the previous spring, it would not be surprising if there were a surplus of dogs looking for an area containing vixens. Older dog foxes that have bred successfully in previous years will probably re-establish the same territory as before but there will, I believe, be movement of young dogs in their first season, bachelor dogs from the previous years and probably a few widowers, all looking for vixens. On this theory one would expect that a seasonal movement of dog foxes takes place in late autumn and continues into winter unless all the unattached dogs rapidly find a stamping ground, which is most unlikely.

Is there evidence of any such movement? I think there is and it comes from a variety of sources. The local huntsmen tell me (and it seems to be generally accepted) that dog foxes give the hounds long runs during the winter months and they suggest that these animals are strangers trying to return to their home areas. In North America, a similar phenomenon is observed and trappers never follow the track of a 'traveller', as it is called.

We also have reports of mass trapping of foxes. In Missouri, eighty-six animals were caught on a 640-acre farm in 1950, and thirty-five were trapped from a similar area during ten days in January 1954. In the winter of 1964 a local Gloucestershire farmer shot a large number of foxes which cannot all have been resident in the area.

Russian authors describe mating phases when a large number of dog foxes are seen pursuing a single female. Just how sex identification is made I do not know, but presumably the fact that a large number of individuals are chasing one other is significant and the suggestion plausible.

How many of the foxes caught in Missouri and Gloucestershire were dogs, we are not told, but there is some well-documented evidence from Norway and Germany which helps here. From this we know that, in these two countries at least, far more dog foxes than vixens are killed in winter, so it is not unreasonable to suppose that the bulk of the moving foxes are dogs. In all, I think the case for mass movements by foxes in late autumn and early winter is fairly well established, though we need more information about the sexes of foxes killed at different times of the year to make absolutely certain that the dogs are the wanderers.

If I am correct in my belief that the dog foxes move into strange areas in their quest for sexual fulfilment, they will, of course, often come across well-established territories and will only be able to fill in, as it were, vacant lots or defeat a resident dog. Hence many dog foxes are probably forced into a celibate state and their only chance of covering a vixen may come at the end of the main rut when young females in their first season are coming on heat. It is probably then that most of the reported mating chases take place.

I see dog-fox territories, therefore, as being rather stable, defended areas containing one or usually more vixens, depending upon the suitability of the area for den construction. When vixens are plentiful, the resident dog is definitely polygamous; when there is a shortage of vixens in his area he may be monogamous. The reservoir of male foxes only finds an outlet when territorial dogs die, are defeated or become too old actively to defend an area. Probably most of the moving dog population each winter is killed by man, his traps and his dogs; only the stronger, fortunate few, dog foxes manage to find and establish territory to claim as their own and in which they continue to live after the rut.

What about the vixens? I think their territorial ambitions are slight compared with those of their spouses. Although scenting takes place, the purpose is probably to establish a social hierarchy, after which a number of vixens can and do live close together fairly peacefully. Work in the United States suggests that foxes' breeding dens are at their greatest density on sloping ground and it may be that these are the most sought-after habitats because the vixens find more suitable earths in such situations.

What is the evidence for a vixen social organisation? As I have said, in 1964 three vixens produced litters in the Kent's Green area and in the same year I had a report of three Worcestershire vixens producing litters under one pig house that measured 14 × 9 ft! There are also Russian and American reports of loose colonies of foxes breeding close to one another, and of two vixens having their cubs in one earth. The litters are often of slightly different age and there is occasionally a great age difference between two neighbouring sets of cubs.

My theory for the vixens is that in September, October and early November those which have bred in an area shoo off the offspring by using the same alarm call they used earlier in the year to warn those same cubs of danger. The calls are single piercing yells of the 'wo-wo-ough' type, rising to a scream on the third syllable.

Scenting and screaming, I think, establish the 'pecking order' among vixens living very close to one another, the nett result being a stable, very loose community of vixens living around a suitable number of breeding earths. Social position is probably established each autumn and spring; in October the vixens take over an earth and live in it, and it may be that when earths are in short supply more than one vixen will use an earth, each at the same time no doubt retaining its individual social rank.

After the rut is over—at the end of January at Kent's Green—the dog foxes seem almost to retire from very active life for a few weeks and certainly do not, in my experience, continue to maintain their territory so far as scenting and barking are concerned. The dog now ranges over the wider area that I call its home range, sharing many parts of it with other foxes both male and female but relying upon scent as the 'social spacer' to achieve separation.

But if dog-fox territory is, as I suggest, a transient seasonal phenomenon, this is far from being the case with the hierarchical vixen community around the dens. Vixens maintain their social structure probably during the whole of the year. During the spring, when the vixen is, in my opinion, totally responsible for feeding the cubs, there is a consequent high vixen mortality rate. As we know from recent work published about the Scottish fox, there is an extremely rapid turn-over in the vixen population and few survive two or three breeding seasons. There are, therefore, many vacancies for young vixens to fill each autumn and they do not have to travel far from their birthplace to establish themselves. There is, consequently, a lower mortality rate for them in autumn and winter; they are also, as I have suggested, less active in the daytime during winter than the dog foxes, which would further tend to protect them.

How much social contact there may be between members of the opposite sex I do not know, though I suspect it is very slight except during the actual breeding season. Some observers and writers claim that the dog fox feeds the vixen both before and after the cubs are born and that he is a most attentive father. In support of this the photograph at Plate 12a depicts the transfer of food from dog to vixen, the sexes being known as they were captive animals. I do not doubt that this may occur occasionally in the wild also, but I do question whether it is of general occurrence. A dog fox that procures only one vixen in a season might perhaps help feed his offspring, but on my theory of territory and taking the dog to be polygamous on most occasions, he would not physically be able to help with a heavy family responsibility.

Mating
and Family Life

Though copulation among wild foxes is very rarely observed and generally believed to take place at night, my field-sign reading indicates that it occurs in middle to late January. All we can do is to note when cubs appear at the entrance to earths or are dug out by farmers and if we then guess at their age—which we can do to within a week or so—we have an approximate idea of their date of birth. Assuming the gestation period for wild foxes to be the same as for captive silver foxes, that is, fifty-one to fifty-two days, we can then by extrapolation arrive at a date of conception which should be within a day or two at most from copulation. With so many unknowns and approximations, it is not surprising that a variety of answers are given to the question: when do foxes mate?

Anatomical studies of male foxes in Indiana tell us that they are capable of fertilising a vixen between 20 December and 10 February. Ranch foxes are fertile and produce sperm only between late November and mid-March, at least in the northern hemisphere, while in Australia male foxes are infertile between September and March, and so presumably fertile for approximately five months (McIntosh, 1964). In the British Isles, most male foxes are fertile between December and February (Reed, 1960), though some old males are probably fertile as early as November.

From this information, from a wide variety of sources, we at least know there is a period in the year when dog foxes are incapable of fertilising vixens. Vixens, for their part, seem to be receptive to the dog foxes for only three weeks of the year, and of these twenty-one days or so they can only be fertilised on three or four of them (Tembrock, 1957).

The timing of this infertile period in any individual fox is partly dependent upon its age, young foxes of both sexes in their first season tending to reach reproductive condition slightly later in the year than their elders. This means there will be an overlap of fertile periods to which we cannot give precise dates in a population of foxes. The older vixens in the population will come into heat earlier than the first-season females and so produce the early litters, some even in December. From my experience in Gloucestershire, it seems that the earlier litters are born on high ground which, as we have seen, may often provide the most suitable breeding earths.

With a high juvenile percentage in the population, one would expect a later average breeding date, and this may partly explain the later breeding of the Scottish foxes compared with their English cousins. For we know there is a very rapid turnover in the Scottish vixen population, 60 per cent of the vixens killed at earths in spring being young (Douglas, 1965). Few vixens, in fact, seem to survive for more than two seasons in regions where foxes are dug out during the spring.

Actual date of birth of the cubs will vary according to latitude, age of the vixens, and probably also local weather conditions. In France as a whole, pregnant foxes can be found in most months of the year (Bernard, 1959), whereas in the British Isles the start of the rut varies from November in southern England to about a month later in Scotland. I believe that the onset of the rut is marked by the beginning of the 'wo-wo' type of barking, which in Gloucestershire begins on high ground in November and reaches a climax in the lowland in early January.

At Kent's Green, I have first seen cubs outside the earths in early April, which would give the birth date as sometime in early March and a copulation time in mid-January. This agrees well with my field-sign reading and is the time of most intense trail scenting and dropping, as well as vocal activity. After mating, the vocal and general field sign declines rapidly; the vixens, who have by this time probably prepared an earth for their cubs, settle down to a solitary pregnancy, while the dog moves off to recuperate from its loss of weight and condition during the two months or so of the rutting period.

Size of Litter

When developing young (embryos) are counted in the vixen's uterus, a much better idea of the potential litter size can be obtained than by counting actual cubs at earths. This is because pre-natal and immediate post-natal deaths would not, of course, be taken into account in a direct field count of cubs at earths.

The maximum potential litter size so far recorded seems to be the thirteen from a uterine count on a North American red fox. Any higher number than this, and probably anything over eight cubs found living together, is due to communal denning, and it is by no means unusual to have two litters in one earth.

In foxes, resorption of the embryos, which seems to be so common in rabbits, is rare, but a pre-natal mortality of about 22 per cent has been found, due to loss of some of the fertilised eggs before they become attached to the wall of the uterus by the placenta (pre-placentation loss of egg or blastocyst) (McIntosh, 1964).

The developing young are usually distributed equally between the two branches of the uterus, a feature brought about partly at least by migration of the developing egg from one side of the uterus to the other (transuterine migration) (Creed). Whatever the potential number of the fox's litter, the number born is on average between four and five, and there are generally slightly more male cubs born than female.

Time-table of Events in the Cub's life

From various sources: Burton, Rowland & Park (1935), Tembrock, Lund & McIntosh

Age	Weight	Event
	100 gm	Birth.
10 days		Eyes open.
4 weeks		First appear outside breeding den with chocolate woolly coats (Fig 16a).
6 weeks	1,130 gm	Red coat colour develops (Fig 16b).
7 to 9 weeks		Cubs weaned and leave earths permanently.
12 weeks		Begin to become independent (Fig 16c).
14 weeks		Cubs independent. Family begins to break up.
4½ months	3,160 gm	
25 weeks		Adult size but not weight.
7 months		Complete development of full winter coat.
9 months		Sexually mature.
		Winter following birth full grown.

16. As the cubs grow older, the face and relative position of the ears change markedly (a) Four-week-old cub; (b) six-week-old cub; (c) ten-week-old cub (from photographs).

FAMILY LIFE

As suggested in the previous chapter, selection of the natal earth is probably made in the October before the cubs are born and the vixen then takes up residence there. Unlike badgers, the vixen does not provide any bedding material for the cubs to lie on, but as they are born with a woolly, chocolate brown coat this, presumably, is not a disadvantage. They are blind for about the first ten days of life and seem to be suckled below ground for the first month of life (Plate 12b). During this time the vixen kennels with her cubs and I have watched vixens emerge from their earths in March. After this first month below ground, the cubs begin to come above ground when the vixen leaves them for her evening forage. At first, they just appear at the entrance as she departs and return below ground once she has gone (Plate 13a). A few days later they are more bold and begin to play at the entrance after the vixen has left, gradually becoming more adventurous. The cubs may now move between adjacent entrances to the earths, indulge in mock combats on the way or just sit together at the entrance to the earth and watch (Plate 13b).

One evening in Big Pit I watched four cubs sitting in a row in the dusk looking up at a bat that was circling the nearby trees. As the bat circled, so did the heads of the cubs and when they briefly faced me I could clearly see four small white chests momentarily turned in my direction. When a jet aircraft flew over, the cubs showed no consternation and continued their usual activities.

The area around the earth soon begins to show signs of the fox family's presence; old tree stumps show small scratch marks on the soft timber, narrow trails are worn in the vegetation around the earth and, of course, food remains and droppings give an untidy look to the area.

Cub activities sometimes go on throughout the day, even though the vixen may be kennelling beneath ground only a few yards away. She is either unaware that the cubs are above ground or is not unduly concerned. Apart from mock combats—during which one cub will straddle another as they attempt to bite each other's ears and neck— digging and chewing at anything 'chewable' are the main preoccupations. Beetles are uncovered and watched with obvious interest, moths and flies are snapped at and bits of grass eaten. Often, only

144

one member of the family will be active, and one gets the impression that even at the tender age of one month some individuals in a litter are quite bold and seem to dominate the activity of the litter. Male cubs are generally heavier than females in the same litter, and it may be the young dog foxes that are dominant.

When the cubs are about six weeks old, the vixen leaves them in the natal den and kennels by herself some little distance away. She does not, in my experience, warn the cubs of approaching danger; many times I have walked up to an earth, sat down and within a few minutes the cubs I disturbed have reappeared and, after casting a few glances in my direction, continued where they left off. If one approaches slowly the cubs may not even retreat but just look towards the intruder and carry on with their play.

My first knowledge of a family living in Clewes' Pond Earth in May 1966 came when I disturbed a vixen that appeared to be lying up in the brambles around the north end of the pond. The time was 6.20 am on 2 May. I investigated the earths and found them all to be in use, many small footprints confirming the presence of cubs, or that they had been there recently.

On the 13th I was sitting high in a tree near Big Pit, from which point I could cover much of the area by eye. At 3.45 pm I saw the buff-tipped vixen I had disturbed on the 2nd crossing a field and making towards Clewes' Pond Earth. I climbed down from my tree and quickly made my way towards Three Oaks Pit, from where I hoped to gain another view of the fox, but I was unlucky. With nothing much to lose, I decided to approach the earth towards which the vixen appeared to be heading and, after crossing the large field near the earth, I saw her with a cub that had run out to meet her. The vixen stood for a few seconds and I believe the cub briefly suckled her, then both animals disappeared from view into a slight depression near the earth. I walked swiftly across the rest of the field towards the earth and, seeing the vixen appear again only a few yards away, I flung myself to the grass. She had not noticed my far from subtle approach for when I looked up she was standing and again a cub was suckling—only about ten yards away from me.

The vixen then moved off by herself on a trail that would soon bring her to my cross-field track. She appeared to be hunting in the grass—a lean, slender animal with this peculiar yellow-buff tail tag. With ears back and keeping very close to the ground, she trotted quickly until she reached my fresh trail, at which she stopped, backed a little and crouched. After a few seconds of looking about her, she finally crossed my trail and confidently went across the open field until she got down wind of me as I lay in the grass with binoculars trained on her. This precipitated a crisis for now, with head up, she abandoned her trail and set off at a gallop into the nearest hedge and away beyond. She made no noise and after she had gone I walked to the earth and was able to watch two of her cubs fighting. The vixen obviously recognised human scent very close to her cubs and yet did nothing about it. Just how good a mother is the vixen? On this evidence, a bad one, or do we expect this animal to be much more cunning and perceptive than she really is?

I was to have another memorable watch that same evening, this time at Savage's Grange Earth. At 8.30 pm when I arrived, the light was good and I at once saw two cubs running across some old straw that had been dumped near the earth. They moved across to the nearby orchard, where they were soon joined in vigorous play by three other cubs. As usual, there was much chasing and tail lashing, but a new activity to me was a stiff-legged leaping by two cubs around a tree trunk. This is the nearest approach to vulpine 'peepbo' I have seen; short yaps were the only noises that accompanied these activities.

At dusk, a vixen with a prominent white tail tag, 'White-Tip', joined the cubs on their play ground. The cubs immediately surrounded her and, with the vixen in the van, began a series of short, rapid chases across the orchard. With much yapping and screeching the foxes appeared then disappeared from view, the play coming to an abrupt end when the vixen stood still and then started to swing round in a circle, holding something in her mouth. I assumed she had brought food to the cubs and was making them jump to get it but after much squealing and yapping the vixen loosed the object which immediately picked itself up, for it was a cub. Another cub was then picked up, apparently by the tail, and similarly swung round, finally loosed and so on. If I had not seen this actually happening I doubt if I would readily have believed a report of it; nor were we finished yet for the swinging game, if that is what it was, then became almost a running battle between cubs and adult. This eventually brought the family through the hedge, out on to the hard surface of the lane and almost to my feet in a twirling mass of fur and yelps. All ended far too quickly for my liking when the vixen caught my scent, growled and, with the cubs in tow, hiccupped her way back into the orchard.

She did not retreat far, but sat in the gathering darkness about twenty-five yards away from me. I had not moved during the retreat and vixen and I now stared at each other—I through my binoculars—for a considerable time—it may have been as long as ten minutes. Whilst we stared, the cubs continued to play, and it ended when the vixen again joined in the chases and they all moved out of sight. The whole watch had lasted one hour and ten minutes.

This was yet another occasion when I have been surprised at the speed with which a fox will resume normal activities after a considerable fright, and how quickly the animal seems to forget the incident, even to the extent of leaving cubs to their own devices without making sure that the source of danger has disappeared. I suspect, however, that I am surprised because the fox does not react as a human being would to the situation; I expect the fox to be a reasoning animal, which it most certainly is not.

The evening play session with the cubs is a marked feature of family behaviour in May. Cubs are taken a hundred yards or so from the earth by the vixen but are returned before she goes away to forage about half an hour later. Remains of birds with cub droppings at some distance from the earth seem to indicate that the cubs are being fed away from the earths, at least some of the time.

Towards the end of May, the vixens seem to give up daytime feeding of the cubs and this may coincide with the complete weaning. I have previously mentioned the suggestion that the adults may regurgitate semi-digested food to the cubs and Douglas reports having found milk and half-digested vole remains in a cub stomach. Wolves are known to do this and I think it highly probable it is also the case in foxes, for I have only occasionally seen a vixen bringing prey to her cubs. Obviously, the amount of material that could be carried in the jaws would depend upon its relative bulk, and whereas one trip with a rabbit or pigeon would provide enough food for a litter, it would take a large number of trips to provide enough small mammals of vole size to satisfy the same litter. If the food is retained in the stomach, a much greater amount of food, consisting of small items such as beetles and worms, could be brought.

During May, the vixen sometimes warns the cubs of any danger she has detected by giving a yell bark repeated a number of times. Sometimes these calls have awoken us in the early hours of the morning, as the fox did a circuit of our cottage and the neighbouring farm buildings. A vixen may also sometimes move her cubs from one earth to another, perhaps because of disturbance, or because the earths are getting too small for the growing cubs, or simply to widen the cubs' experience of the country.

As has many times been stated, foxes are poor housekeepers and the ground around the earth becomes at times a rather revolting mass of animal bones and feathers; these sometimes fill small blind holes near the main earths and there are always a quantity of cub droppings to be found both in and around the earth entrances. The distance moved by the family is seldom great, being of the order of a quarter to half a mile in my area. Vixens will remove the bodies of cubs that have been gassed below ground, as was the case with three litters that were found and gassed under a pig house in Worcestershire.

By the end of May, it is much more difficult to watch cubs in the daytime as they tend to emerge later in the evening. Occasionally, one sees a solitary cub coming away from the earth at about 8.30 pm but they seem in general to be crepuscular.

An entry in my fieldbook for 23 May 1966, reads:

> Arrived at Clewes' Pond Earth 8.20 pm. Wind slight from the west after strong gusty day but quite warm. Wind dropped as night fell. Cubs appeared from beneath roots of the tree next to the one in which I was sitting. Two came out first, both had white tail tips. Rather a cautious emergence—one looked up at me but apparently on seeing me took no notice. Both moved along the side of the pond to the main earth in dense bramble thicket. Slightly later a third cub appeared and followed the other two. A few minutes later a fourth cub joined them—all had white tail tags —and passed right beneath me, a vertical distance of about ten feet.

> I was glad of my loose scalp tonight in that I was able to dislodge mosquitoes that alighted on my forehead—a use at last for wrinkles!

> I was sitting in rather an uncomfortable position but one forgets this when foxes are about. The cubs occasionally came out on to the grass of the adjoining field and appeared to be waiting for the vixen. Possibly an adult arrived at about 10.20 pm and loud crunching of bones rose up to me from the bramble thicket. Two cubs passed beneath me again and played in the field above the earth.

> Earlier in the evening, before the cubs appeared, there was much scolding from blackbirds and magpies, then a large tawny owl came and sat very close to me in the tree. The owl, rather than the foxes, seemed to be the object of the other birds' displeasure. Probably much of the evening bird-warning notes are directed at

owls rather than prowling foxes, to which birds appear to pay little heed.

Left tree at about 10.35 pm. Fairly new moon and a heavy dew now.

With the end of May, it is time to abandon tree sittings over earths, for they tend to be rather unproductive and the cubs, now about eight to nine weeks old, become much more independent of the adults. Studies on a captive colony show that the cubs tend to leave the earths permanently about seven to eight weeks after birth, and my field evidence supports this, plus a week or so. June at Kent's Green, therefore, sees the abandonment of the earths, the cubs then living in dense hedge bottoms.

Hurrell recommends the would-be watcher of foxes to locate a litter at an earth in June or July. This might be possible on Dartmoor, where it would seem that cubs are born later than in other parts of the country, but I would say the two most profitable months for watching at earths are April and May, certainly no later.

The independence of the cubs can be gauged by the number of occasions on which I bumped into solitary cubs wandering along at quite long distances from their homes. I have seen cubs in the early morning, just before 7 am, returning to the hedges in which they live. Independence is also reflected in their diet, which now consists largely of food items obtainable by the cub's own devices, although still containing some items brought by the adult. The vixens are not now seen in the daytime but become active about 8 pm, and seem to leave food items, such as birds, at a little distance from the hedges.

I do not subscribe to the view that the adult foxes teach the cubs how to catch prey. As we have seen, the vixen does take the cubs away from the earth in May but only, it seems, to introduce them to new terrain by playing and chasing about in different areas. Is a cat taught to catch mice by its mother? Certainly not, in my experience of cats. It is true some cats are more interested in mousing than others, but ability to capture moving objects seems to be inherited rather than taught by parents, and I think the same applies to the fox. We know it applies to weasels in captivity. From watching fox cubs I am convinced that food procuring is learned by trial and error only. Any and every object is sniffed at and, if it does not react by running away too fast or hurting the cub's soft nose, then an attempt is made to eat or at least chew it. By performing these operations, the cub soon learns by experience to associate some smells with desirable, thus consumable, food, whilst others will be rejected as either inedible or unpalatable. The amount of trash eaten by cubs bears witness to the experimentation which takes place.

In June, the play areas are very obvious, particularly in mowing grass, and it is in such places that cubs can now best be watched. They are usually at the side or in the corner of a field not very far from the hedge in which the cubs live, and here they play, eat and defecate and are visited by the vixen at nightfall. Hedge bottoms, in which the cubs spend the day, are thick and often have a ditch which the cubs use as a highway; in a dry summer this soon becomes littered with droppings and bird feathers.

In July and August, independence of the cubs seems to become absolute, though they continue to perform their nightly romp just after emerging and at times these can be very vocal activities. On 5 July 1964 I was standing in Savage's orchard by Little Pond Earth with my back to a tree watching two hares feeding. At 9.35 pm, as it was getting dim, I heard a noise which I described in my fieldbook as sounding like owls or cats fighting. The noise came from the next field that had recently been mown, before which it had a very well-marked cub play area in one corner. The shrieks and squeals were punctuated occasionally by sharp yaps. Using the natural cover available I crawled past the earth and up the bank in which it was dug, to the field above. After negotiating the barbed wire of the fence, I slowly and carefully stood up to see long, arrow-like shapes moving in the middle of the mown field. There were four cubs playing energetically amongst the cut grass. Stiff-legged springing was a common movement and reminded me of the adults' pounce when 'voling'. The squeals were produced as one cub nipped another in a tender spot, and it was noticeable that two individuals did most of the chasing about. An adult fox then appeared on the far side of the field, quickly made its way towards the cubs but seemed hardly to notice them, and as quickly disappeared into the hedge.

The cubs then moved away from the middle of the field to the far side, down a slight depression and so out of view. I was about to make towards home when suddenly a cub came bounding towards me; I stood very still near the hedge and the cub kept coming until it was about ten yards from me. It looked in my direction, slightly changed course and crossed my wind about five yards from me; it then poked its head through the hedge into the next field. The cattle on the other side must have frightened the cub for it shot backwards and bounded back across the hayfield the way it had come. Its line of travel was broken once as it leaped sideways and pounced on a pile of hay. No doubt a vole had made a noise and the cub had tried unsuccessfully to capture it.

The following morning I returned to the same field and was again able to see three cubs playing in the hay, again with the stiff-legged leaps I had seen the night before. At about 7.30 am, the cubs chased each other over to the thick hedge near the earth and presumably settled down for the day. They would seem, therefore, to be active from about 9.30 pm to 7.30 am, although doubtless they occasionally rest during this time.

A family of cubs seems to stay together until at least early September, after which usually one or two cubs are seen at a time. It seems likely that the fighting so often seen, and particularly heard, during July and August, has much to do with the break up, for it often appears to be much more than 'good clean fun'.

My last glimpses of the cubs have been usually in September, after which it is very difficult to tell grown cubs from adults, as foxes are seldom seen in good light in the autumn.

On 22 September 1964 I was again in the orchard but this time in a tree. At 7.20 pm I saw a grown cub emerge from the hedge next to Savage's Pond Earth; it began to eat the fallen pears and was soon joined by a second cub. The first cub remained quietly eating but the newcomer galloped across the orchard, through the hedge into a field with bullocks, and then back again into the orchard. The gallop was interrupted by slight pauses during which the cub lashed its tail from side to side, a movement which also took place during the galloping. Both cubs then began eating, until a bellow from the neighbouring bullocks sent them rushing helter skelter to the hedge for cover.

How does the family break up and how much of a family is there to break up?

It has been suggested that the fox parents protect and educate their offspring. Protect they may do by removing cubs from disturbed earths but any evidence of education is, I think, far from established. It is true, as we have seen, that vixens take the cubs away from the earths for short trips of a hundred yards or so and the purpose of these excursions may well be to provide the cubs with experience of as many different aspects of their environment as possible. We also know that an animal which, during its infancy, is not confined to a small area offering little diversification of activities or experiences, has a greater intelligence than would otherwise be the case. And certainly a fox cub is brought into contact with a number of earths during its first few weeks of life and so is able to explore, with the vixen's prompting, a diversity of habitats. But there is no evidence to support the contention that the adults teach the cubs to hunt and kill prey. During the summer there are plenty of small food items that a cub can easily learn to eat by trial and error. These include worms, beetles, caterpillars and moths among animals, and grass and fruit amongst the plants, and it is my belief that the ability of a cub to survive to maturity is dependent upon its instinctive skill to capture prey, an art that develops with age.

This conclusion is, I know, far less 'interesting' than the popular belief that the vixen takes the cubs out and introduces them to all the edible things in their environment, while warning them of potential dangers. The idea that the adults at first bring disabled prey to the cubs to kill and then go on to teach them how to locate and capture rabbits and mice, is intriguing, but, I think, most improbable. It is often said that adult foxes bury food for the cubs to find and that this trains them to use their sense of smell. The alleged evidence for this is that foxes have frequently been seen burying food but, as we have already seen, caching surplus food occurs throughout the year, particularly in winter. It, therefore, seems to me to be merely fortuitous if a cub finds food that an adult has buried, and I cannot believe it represents a conscious attempt on the part of the adult to educate its young.

Again, according to Brian Vesey-Fitzgerald a fox will not pass beneath wire and he says that a vixen teaches her cubs to associate wire with danger. He suggests that this acquired knowledge is passed on from one generation to the other by the vixen. Yet I have watched both 'Buff Tip' and 'White Tip' pass under wire fences, and only by doing so could they reach their earths. Furthermore, the number of foxes trapped in wires each year suggests that any such communication between vixen and cubs cannot be very efficient.

Nor do I believe that vixens educate their cubs to forage in the way often suggested. Stalking and pouncing behaviour can be seen in even the youngest cubs, once they are at the earth entrance. They learn what to pounce on and what not, what is hurtful and what edible simply by trial and error. Beetles are found under cow dung merely because the cub is inquisitive enough to dig into it, and the variety of articles I have found in cub droppings indicates that almost anything will be sampled—bootlaces, rubber bands, earth and bits of metal. There is no indication at all that the adult educates the cubs in what and what not to eat, nor in devices to help them catch prey. The earlier chapter on food showed that the cub's early diet is rich in small mammals and birds but that as they begin to find food for themselves (which they do almost as soon as they appear at the entrance to the earth), the proportion of insects, grass, worms and other easily-procured prey rapidly increases until it comprises almost the whole diet.

There is also a summer low of mammals in the adults' diet which occurs when they should, according to the 'vixen education school', be teaching cubs 'the ways of mice, voles and rabbits' and one would therefore expect to find a fair proportion of such beasts occurring in both adult and cub droppings. The fact that they do not does not surprise me for, as I have said, the fox is essentially a creature which feeds on the most easily obtained food, and in the summer voles do not come into this category whilst fruit, insects and, to a lesser extent, birds do. In autumn, when mammal remains occur frequently in the droppings, the cubs have left the company of the adults and are independent, so any ability to capture small mammals would seem to be natural and not learned from adults.

Defence of the cubs from human predators is poorly developed in foxes. When a vixen with cubs is disturbed she gives, as we have seen, a low growl and a hiccup which sends the cubs to cover, and she then moves away, leaving them to their own devices. She very rarely stays with them should the danger become acute. One might have expected that the vixen would at least attempt to defend the cubs or else draw the potential attacker after her away from the cubs. She does neither, in my experience, but retreats after giving a vocal warning. On one occasion the buff-tip vixen did not even do this but ran off without a sound so that I was able to go to the earth she had just left and sit down quietly to watch her cubs. Not, I suggest, an example of a female fearlessly defending her young; she did not even attempt to come back to the earth to see if her cubs were safe, neither did she move the cubs, even though this type of encounter between human and herself near the earth had taken place twice before. I might add that this type of behaviour was not confined to 'Buff Tip' but was also observed in 'White Tip'.

As to the rôle of the dog fox in defending the family, I have no evidence that he ever does. Here again, it is suggested that the dog fox lies up near the earth where the vixen and cubs are living together for the first few weeks after birth and warns the vixen of approaching danger. How then have I and numerous other observers been able to watch very young cubs at the entrance of their earths, either in the company of or absence of their mother? Many times in April and May I have quietly walked up to the earths and either sat down or stood and watched the cubs without any sign of dog fox, or vixen for that matter. I suggest that, far from being a model husband and devoted father, the dog fox is just the opposite and normally takes not the slightest interest in either the vixen or her offspring.

I think that the only real family life takes place while the cubs are at the earth and that the relationship is between mother and offspring. The dog fox may occasionally provide food during the first week or so in the life of the cubs, but he does not share the feeding responsibilities with the vixen. It is the vixen that feeds and plays with the cubs but even this relationship lasts only a few weeks, after which it gradually falls apart. The cubs become more and more independent, the visits of the vixen less frequent and the vigour of cub play increases. This vigour, as I suggested, may well have the effect of driving off some cubs from the litter in August and early September. Possibly, some members of the litter stay together until the mating season when they go their separate ways. We do know that cubs travel long distances when the litter eventually breaks up—tagged juveniles have been known to move thirty miles from their birth area—and this dispersal is, I think, aided by the vixens. Much yelling is heard from the end of July and, as I have suggested, may be directed at rather than to the cubs.

Whatever the mechanism, the cubs do disperse but, to me, there is little real family to break up in the first place and I do not consider the family unit to have much significance in the life cycle of the fox.

Sex Ratio

By sex ratio, we mean the relative numbers of each sex of a species in a population. The convention used is to assign a figure of 100 to the number of females of a species and calculate the number of males relative to this. A sex ratio above 100 indicates a surplus of males.

Sex ratios can be of three types:

Primary: the ratio found in embryos just after conception.
Secondary: the ratio at birth—cub ratio.
Tertiary: the ratio of mature animals.

These ratios vary considerably in some animals and each presumably reflects the survival potential of the sexes at various stages in their existence. The tertiary and secondary ratios are the most readily observed, although the amount of reliable data about both is small. Talbot claims that some litters are all male, others female, but overall he says that three out of five are male, giving a sex ratio of 166. Lionel Edwards says that, almost invariably, there are more males than females in a litter. Out of six he claims, two will be females, a sex ratio of 300. The predominance of males over females in a litter is a generally-held view amongst country and hunting people. The only real way to find the exact primary and secondary sex ratio is to examine in a representative area all the specimens of the species concerned. This does not seem to have been done so far. Norwegian foxes do show a surplus of males and an overall ratio of 120 was found, 116 for cubs and adults 123. From the literature concerning English foxes, it appears that a similar surplus of male cubs exists, although the quoted sex ratios are probably far too high as they are not based on a suitable sample of the population.

Secondary sex ratios have been given as 116 in Norway, from 201 cubs examined (Lund); 100 in North America for new-born cubs (Richards and Sheldon) and for captive silver foxes, 109 in Norway and 112 in Sweden (Johansson). From Scotland, however, of eighty-two cubs examined by Douglas, 54 per cent were female and in the two years of his study females were more common than male cubs; only in one year was a surplus of males recorded. The secondary sex ratio for Scottish cubs on the figures available would seem to be eighty-six. In Australia, a cub sex ratio of 114 was found by McIntosh.

The tertiary sex ratio seems to vary greatly according to the season in which the material is collected. This applies at least in Norway and Germany, the only two countries from which suitable information is available (given in Lund). Around mid-winter, there is a large surplus of males killed, whilst in the spring and summer a distinct surplus of females is found. In Scotland, twice as many females as males are killed by fox hunters, but this is presumably due to the method of killing which takes place mainly in spring when the earths are flushed and vixens shot while the cubs are then killed. Very few dog foxes are killed by this form of hunting, and one cannot get a reliable tertiary ratio from such evidence.

From the above, it appears that the fox population, as with other members of the family *Canidae*, generally has a surplus of males.

Ecology

Ecological niche

If we look at a field hedge we first see the most obvious characteristics, the trees and bushes, but these are not the only plants present in such a habitat. Climbers such as 'traveller's joy' (*Clematis vitalba*) and bryony (*Bryonia dioica*), ramblers such as dog rose (*Rosa canina*) and leavers (*Calium aparine*), bring diversity to what may originally have been a simple stand of hawthorn.

Among the vegetation, insects and birds make their homes and different types of insects live on their own favourite host plant. Some birds will nest at the base of the hedge amongst the matted grass and herbs, others will build in the bushes themselves. Large birds build in the trees of the hedgerow, either inside hollow trunks or on branches; climbing ivy on the trees provides smaller birds with nesting places. Caterpillars eat leaves and some sew them together to form shelters. Wood-boring insects live beneath the bark of the tree, as do fungi, woodlice and a host of other small animals. Squirrels in trees, woodmice climbing at night among the lower branches and along twig highways, bank voles burrowing in the leaf mould and soft earth at the hedge base, shrews hurrying along vegetation tunnels, rabbits and badgers in larger tunnels—all can be found in the shelter of the hedge. Among this apparent confusion there is an element of order, at least so far as food supply for the many organisms is concerned. No two animals have exactly the same requirements or, if they have similar ones, they satisfy them in different positions in the hedge. Insect-eating birds of different species layer themselves—blue tits at the tops of the hedge, great tits in the base and on the ground underneath. Bank voles and woodmice eat similar nuts and berries, but the mice can climb to collect these and use an old bird's nest in which to feed and rest; a bank vole is confined to the ground where it eats the fruits as they fall and stores its food underground, as does the woodmouse on occasions. The result of this diversification is that no two animals living in one habitat, in this case the hedge, overlap completely in their daily needs for space or food.

There are carnivorous animals, spiders eating insects at one end of the scale and badgers eating voles at the other; vegetarians of all kinds; scavengers—from beetles to magpies; parasites, both plant and animal—they all occupy slightly different positions in the economy of the hedge; to use a biological expression, they occupy different niches in their environment. All are interdependent in some way and a drastic change in one section may have wide repercussions.

The number of small vegetarians in the hedge is vast, the number of small carnivorous animals feeding on them is smaller and the number of large carnivorous animals is smaller still. This phenomenon was described by Elton (1927) as a pyramid of numbers. The base of the pyramid is composed of the many small vegetarians and the apex is occupied by the large carnivorous animals.

The fox, in our case, is the apex of the pyramid, but it is a scavenger as well as an important predator and, as we have seen, is better thought of as an omnivorous animal consuming anything edible and available. Foxes fit into their niche in the environment just as perfectly as do other natural members of the society. Because they fit, they have little total effect on the surrounding population of animals, provided those animals are there in normal density. A fox on farmland in Gloucestershire takes very few ground-nesting birds, such as partridge and pheasant, because they are not easily detected or caught. If the density of these species is increased artificially, then the fox is bound to do damage, at least so far as man is concerned, but for the birds this predation is good, keeping their numbers in equilibrium with the available food supplies.

It seems to me a fox will kill anything which is available to it and unable to defend itself in some way. This does not make it a cold-blooded killer, killing just for the sake of it, at least not in my view. People have often said to me: 'Why did the fox have to kill all the hens instead of just taking one, which would have been quite sufficient?' This question, while seeming reasonable, rests on a false premise, namely, that the fox 'knows' how much food it can eat at a meal. We may equally have asked why a lion kills a zebra, which it cannot possibly eat completely, when a small antelope would have satisfied its appetite just as well. The fox or the lion catches and kills whatever is available, and many other animals depend on their kills. On the lion's kill will feast jackals, hyaenas and vultures, together with a host of other animals, including many species of insect. We must look at the animal's actions in relation to its position in the food chain and not consider a kill to be a waste of life, satisfying only one individual fox or lion. Can we say the same of ourselves when we kill and eat a chicken and incinerate the carcass and other remains?

But let us return to the hen-house full of dead fowl, with only one body missing. It is a waste so far as we are concerned but if we choose to set up an artificially crowded population and do not take adequate precautions to exclude predators, we must accept the consequences. It is man who is upsetting the natural distribution of animals and we must not be surprised if nature, in the form of the fox, tries to correct the disturbance. Pheasants and foxes live side by side in the wild state—some of the former survive and the breeding stock is kept healthy by the removal of weaklings and badly-adapted individuals. Predators and scavengers are just as vital to a healthy community of animals as are the aesthetically more pleasing vegetarians; they are all links in a chain.

As we have seen, the picture of the fox as primarily a sheep and poultry eater is incorrect, at least so far as the lowland fox in England is concerned. It performs a useful rôle in rodent eating, and in the course of a year an individual fox accounts for a large number of field voles *Microtus agrestis*. As a scavenger, the fox helps to keep the countryside free from carcasses by performing the initial breaking up of bodies, a task completed by a variety of insects and birds.

How much effect the fox has upon wild rodent population I do not

L   159

know but, as I have said, it is unlikely to be great (Plate 14a). Fox predation on small mammals is greatest in autumn when their numbers are high, and least during the summer when small mammals are building up their population. Late winter predation certainly would reduce the breeding stock for the next spring and at least ensure that those left had plenty of room and food to increase their chances of successful breeding. The summer build-up in the population is hardly affected by fox predation and I suspect that if the fox has a rôle in keeping, say, the number of voles in check, it does so when the vole population is in a critical position between March and June, and not when they are abundant. In other words, they may prevent a rapid build up of numbers rather than control the numbers once they are in existence.

Since wolves disappeared from this country in the eighteenth century, the adult fox has had no real enemies apart from man. Cubs are occasionally taken by golden eagles in Scotland, and also, it is said, by badgers. There is evidence of the former but I know of none to confirm the badger as a fox-cub predator. The number of foxes would, therefore, seem to be limited only by natural death brought about by parasites in some cases, man with his dogs and guns, not to mention snares and poison gas. In this country it is highly unlikely that any shortage of food causes the deaths of adults except in exceptionally severe winters, such as 1962–3, but even then so many birds, either dead or dying, are available that the number of fox mortalities must be small.

The condition of the fox is, however, partly determined by available food supply, particularly in the period up to midwinter. In late autumn and early winter we have seen that the fox is at its heaviest and this is partly due to the accumulation of fat under the pelt and around the entrails. In Norway, about 75 per cent of foxes examined were in peak condition in midsummer and midwinter. There is some evidence that the average weight of foxes can vary from year to year, indicating changes in the condition of the animals (Richards, et al., 1953).

In spring, the condition of the fox seems to be at its poorest for the year; in Norway, only 60 per cent of those examined were in good condition (Lund). A decline in the small rodent population was, in one instance, shown to coincide with the local foxes being in poor condition. In this country, when myxomatosis was at its height and there were few rabbits available for the fox, it was feared that the fox, deprived of its main food item, would increase its attacks on domestic animals. Instead, as Lever (1959) showed and I have confirmed, the field vole became much more important in its diet and there has been no significant increase in domestic animal losses. It would be interesting to carry out a long-term survey in one particular area of the fluctuations in small mammal populations, at the same time keeping a check on the weight and general condition of foxes in the area. It may be that if the English fox continues to be deprived of rabbits, as it is at Kent's Green, a crash in the local population of small mammals could have serious consequences for the fox, at least so far as condition and reproductive ability are concerned. But so long as food from human activities continues to be available to foxes, it is unlikely that fox numbers will be very much influenced by the number of small mammals.

Predator–Prey Relationship

In a natural community of animals, predatory and prey animals live in close proximity to one another with their home ranges overlapping. Small prey species with a restricted home range can only retreat from a predator for a short distance, depending upon the size of the home range. Animals that are preyed upon have a particularly watchful nature and attempt to keep an enemy a set distance from them. This distance is species specific and gives the prey sufficient time to remove themselves from danger should a predator be hunting. At other times they appear to take little notice of a non-hunting predator but remain very alert.

In a wild situation without man, the animals will have no fear of him when he is first encountered, because he is not recognised as a predator. On offshore islands, the indigenous animals may also not associate man with potential danger in that environment at least, and so allow a closer approach than would be tolerated on a nearby mainland.

When man first started to hunt wild animals, the critical distance the animals allowed him was probably not great, due to the limited range of man's early weapons and his relative lack of speed. As more sophisticated weapons with a greater range were developed, the animals man hunted probably increased the critical distance he was allowed. Modern man with firearms is given a very wide berth by wild animals in regions where hunting takes place, and this has probably given rise to the idea that all animals will immediately flee as far as possible from any approaching predator. It would be biologically extremely wasteful in terms of feeding time lost and energy expenditure to do so; animals merely keep a respectful distance apart and seem to accept the inevitable loss of some of their number, as they must if predators are to survive.

The task of the predator, therefore, is to reduce the critical distance that is allowed away from its prey. It can do this in a number of ways:

(a) Reduce in some way the prey's recognition of the predator by behaviour such as feigning death or simply by playing.

(b) Direct chase of the prey, trying to outrun it over a short distance.

(c) By stealth, creeping up on the prey unseen.

I will deal with each method in turn, with particular reference to the fox.

All mammals explore their environment; anything new that is found becomes the object of close attention and may be said to arouse a low level of fear. However, this slight apprehension seems to prompt the animal to investigate the object fully in order to reduce the fear of the unknown in the environment. I suggest this may apply to a rabbit that is watching a fox, or a stoat performing its play antics or so-called dances. The rabbit would probably react to a hunting stoat by keeping a safe distance away, which might involve a retreat underground. A playing stoat or fox does not register as of immediate danger, it only stimulates a low level of fear which releases the drive to explore the phenomenon. We may say in general terms that the predator has a fatal fascination. The dancing predator is now the object of investigation and the rabbit will either approach or else allow the fox to get nearer by its own movements. Once the critical distance is reduced, the predator may be able to pounce upon the nearest rabbit or capture it after a short chase. The change in form of the fox or stoat from a playing source of low-level fear to a hunting predator may release a high level of fear in the rabbit, who is now closer to its enemy than it would normally have allowed. An intense fear reaction is thus produced which may result in the observed reaction of rabbits that just lie and squeal, petrified with fright as we say, so proving easy game for the predator.

Much of this is, of course, highly speculative but it attempts to explain field observations made when rabbits have been captured, much in the way described. This is usually regarded as showing the skill of the fox and the stupidity of the rabbit. But does this necessarily show that the fox is cunning? In my view, it need not but it does indicate that a fox has at least the capacity to learn from experience. We know that solitary carnivorous animals in particular will sometimes indulge in what we call aggressive play directed against an unresponsive animal or object. The fox or stoat does not necessarily intend that its activities shall be of interest to potential prey animals, but should the technique result in a suitable reward in the form of a meal, it may be repeated on other occasions which may, or may not, bring further reward. Play may, therefore, be said in this instance at least to have a biologically useful function in occasionally providing carnivorous animals with food. After all, they are the most playful group of animals next to the primates.

A similar method of reducing the critical distance which a fox could possibly use, is to feign death. We have already seen that the fox, like other animals, does at times sham death as a defensive mechanism and one adopting such a posture might well be the subject of curiosity, if we may use such a term. Birds of the crow family are particularly attentive to new features in their surroundings and a still fox would be most likely to arouse their curiosity. A crow coming too close to such a fox could well find itself attacked and possibly forming a vulpine meal. This activity again, if successful in obtaining a meal for the fox, might be repeated on other occasions, although I think a fox would seldom effect a capture by such a technique.

I have only seen one instance of a fox being mobbed by rooks and that was in June 1966, when the white-tipped vixen was hunting in the grass of Whittal's orchard at about 8 pm. Two rooks made two or three low flights over the fox, which only paused and briefly looked up. The 'attack' soon ceased and the vixen returned to her hunting. In fact, I have been surprised at the little notice birds in general take of a hunting fox. On many occasions I have watched 'Buff Tip', the vixen, walking along in broad daylight and in open situations without ever hearing warning cries from birds or seeing any mobbing.

In the evenings, much vocal activity is heard from birds; robins, wrens, tits, magpies, pheasants, woodpeckers, partridges, jays and particularly blackbirds, all of which emit their alarm notes. I used to think that such activity was indicative of fox prowlings but I now regard it as being mainly directed against owls. In the summer, at least, the foxes are out and about long before most of the alarm notes begin to be heard, and I certainly was not able to locate foxes by noting local concentrations of alarm notes. On one occasion only the cawing of rooks drew my attention to a fox, but I was not sure whether the fox just happened to be visible while I heard the cawing, or if the two events were in fact related.

Seldom, I think, does the fox capture prey by stealth. There are reports of foxes lying in wait for victims and of their stalking cat-like up to a sitting bird or feeding rabbit. Food investigation and snow tracking, however, both point to opportunism being the main attribute of the fox when hunting. Seldom do we find field evidence of foxes actually stalking their prey, or if they do stalk they seldom effect a capture.

Again, food investigation and snow trails tell us that foxes do not normally capture prey which can move quickly. A number of observers have watched foxes chase rabbits, for example, but there seem to be few cases in which an actual capture has been observed. Certainly the fox does not seem capable of catching a hare by out-running and this means of food collection is, I think, relatively un-important. Most prey species seem to be captured either because they are not fast enough to get away, or because they are dug out of their holes, eg, small mammals. Birds are captured either because an incubating bird is discovered by a fox, or because they are injured or young, and therefore poor fliers. Most of the large mammalian prey is carrion, which requires a good nose to detect it rather than any well-developed hunting ability. In other words, the fox seems to be basically a predator of small mammals, taking them as and when available without too much effort.

It is many times stated that a fox will not kill close to the earth in which it produces young. Konrad Lorentz (1954) mentions a case of a shelduck raising a family in an occupied fox earth, and I have seen rabbits almost sharing holes with the local foxes; there are numerous other mentions of similar observations. All sorts of inter-pretations are put upon this phenomenon by people writing about foxes in isolation. It is said to show intelligent conservation of local food supplies (Plate 14 b) for the future use of cubs when they become independent from the parents; but this explanation, together with many others, is probably wide of the mark. Lorentz mentions that this 'truce', if we may term it such, between predator and prey close to their homes is found not only in the fox and other members of the dog family but also amongst birds of prey. Lorentz does not suggest an explanation but he does, I think, give a clue when he describes how a hawk that had lived peacefully with a number of pigeons and other potential prey, one day killed one of these; he suggests the hawk may have done so on seeing the bird flying away. It seems as though the flight from a predator triggers off the urge to chase, and that so long as the prey does not retreat it is relatively safe.

Predators of many types then, do not appear to hunt close to their homes. It is well known that a predator that is not hunting does not induce a flight reaction in prey animals, who just remain at a safe distance.

Population Density

Population density would be expected to relate partly at least to available food supplies. In recently-planted forestry land, a rapid increase in the local vole population has sometimes been observed. This might lead at least to a temporary increase in the number of foxes in the area, preying upon the field vole *Microtus agrestis*. Mature plantations would probably contain less foxes than new or young stands. The presence of many open rides in the new forests, however, would probably allow a greater resident fox population than in a natural closed canopy forest.

American work (Scott & Selko, 1939) has shown that the abundance of fox dens in any area is related to the ground slope, more being found on inclined than on flat ground. This seems to be almost self-evident in that opportunities for den construction are much more limited in flat ground which, often consisting of muddy or marly soil and being poorly drained or intensively cultivated, would make unsuitable conditions for tunnelling. Whether the concentration of breeding sites on sloping ground leads to such a situation having a higher fox population over the whole year, I do not know.

Various methods of determining population density have been attempted, including one (Lord, 1961) in which vixens were captured and splayed, then released, the effect of this on the total population being calculated after the next breeding season. Another method used evidence of fox sign together with den counts (Scott 1940).

In the United States, fox densities of up to twenty per square mile have been found (Korschgen, 1959). By contrast, the population at Kent's Green in the breeding season would seem by direct observation to be approximately four adults per square mile.

Habitat

In fact, however, we know very little about the numbers of foxes in different types of country. Seaton (1929) writing about the American red fox says:

> The unbroken forest seems as little suited to the red fox as is absolute civilisation. It is essentially a species of the half-open country and always increases in the half-settled districts. It is very scarce in the days of the primitive wood . . . appears to increase again as land is abandoned and falls out of cultivation.

What evidence is there for thinking that the fox, at least the red variety, is scarce in virgin woodland? We do know, as Seaton says, that the red fox was rare, indeed it is not mentioned in early American literature although there are references to black foxes. It is thought that most of the American red foxes now present have descended from imported European foxes.

In the British Isles, foxes in general seem to have been rare in the days of the great forests and Brian Vesey-Fitzgerald can find no references to them before the thirteenth century, although from the evidence of cave remains we know them to be present as native animals. It would, therefore, seem that foxes are now much more common than in the days before the great forests of Europe and North America were largely felled and replaced by more open country with much shrub, a habitat in which the fox seems to thrive.

Indirect evidence to support this idea comes from American work on fox diet. Cooke and Hamilton (1944) found that in east New York State the animals most often used as food by the local foxes were all associated with feebly used or entirely abandoned farmland, none were strictly of woodland distribution. In this study, 66 per cent of food species came from brush or early woodland, 22 per cent came from grassland and only 12 per cent from forest.

Direct evidence from Russian work has shown that fox tracks in snow are at their most numerous at edges of woodland (Latvin, 1955), in the European part of the Soviet Union. The number of tracks per ten kilometres was calculated for a variety of habitats:

9·1 tracks per 10 km at the edge of woodland
7·3 tracks per 10 km in young coniferous forests
5·4 tracks per 10 km on ploughland
4·3 tracks per 10 km in deciduous brushwood
4·1 tracks per 10 km in non-arable fields and moorland

2·4 tracks per 10 km in mixed stands of forest
2·2 tracks per 10 km in moss-covered moorland
1·3 tracks per 10 km in plantations
0 tracks per 10 km in newly-cut woodland and older fir forests.

Forestry plantations are often said to harbour large numbers of foxes that invade the surrounding farmland. A high population would, from the above evidence of feeding and track abundance, be expected in young coniferous forests, but as these grow up so it would seem the fox population decreases—the implication being that foxes are very rarely found in mature, man-planted forests or natural forests. Control of foxes may be desirable in young forests but does not seem to be necessary for older stands.

We have already mentioned the suggested correlation between colour phases of the fox and different habitats and have suggested that black, or at least more deeply pigmented, phases of the fox are more commonly found in forests than in open environments. Historical evidence, it would seem, points to the same conclusion since there are early references to American black foxes but not to red while, in Finland, hunting records from the sixteenth century show that the dark phase heterozygote, the cross fox, was then more common than the lighter present-day dominant heterozygote, the black-bellied fox. Two forms of black fox are suggested, one from Canada and the other from Alaska, Russia and Northern Europe. We know that black foxes now comprise only a small minority of the fox population but the presence, or at least suggested presence, of two distinct types with black genes at different loci suggests to me that black foxes were once much more common than they are now.

Drawing this information together, it seems reasonable to say that the fox was scarce as a species in the days of primitive woodland, and that those which were present were probably dominantly black or dark phases of red. As the land has been cleared of trees the red fox phase has become the most abundant, both because the habitat has changed and because predation by man on the attractive black and dark colour phases has tended to reduce the black population as a whole.

The red fox is much more adapted to living in disturbed surroundings produced by the activities of man (Plate 15b) and finds the vast majority of its food, in the form of small rodents, carrion and refuse, in such habitats. This man-made habitat, together with man-provided food from various sources, was the probable cause of the fox population explosion which began when man cleared the land for housing and agriculture, and which shows little, if any, sign of decline in the second half of the twentieth century.

DISEASES OF THE FOX

Foxes are infected with a wide variety of parasites, both ecto-parasites living on the surface of the body, and endoparasites living in the tissues and organs of the body itself. Despite the almost universal presence of parasites, individual foxes seem to suffer little obvious effects.

Worms are the most commonly found parasites in foxes and these are all endoparasites. They are of three main types: tapeworms (*Cestodes*), flukes (*Trematodes*) and round worms (*Nematodes*); a fourth, spiny-headed worms (*Acanthocephala*) being more rarely present. The species and distribution of the various worms is shown in Fig 17, Appendix G, parasites are discussed in Appendix G.

Mortality

Apart from the mortality due to disease amongst the fox popula-tion, most of the annual fox deaths in this country, at least, can be attributed to man, either directly or indirectly. Indirectly, man causes fox deaths by treating cereal seeds with toxic dressings of aldrin, dieldrin and heptachlor pesticides before planting. Birds, as we know only too well, have died in great numbers following con-sumption of the treated seeds. The fox, being the major vertebrate scavenger in the countryside, eats the dead and poisoned birds and this has led to a great number of fox deaths in eastern England; between November 1959 and March 1960, about 1,300 foxes died, mainly in convulsions.

Foxes also seem to be increasingly susceptible to road accidents and over a full year a large number of both adults and cubs are killed, particularly on motorways in the winter months. During my study, I had brought to me the bodies of three foxes killed on local roads—two dog foxes and one vixen, all mature animals. A number of foxes are also killed by stepping on live rails—also the cause of many badger deaths—and at least 50,000 foxes of all ages are esti-mated to be killed each year by hunting, shooting and trapping in the British Isles (Southern, ed, 1964).

Despite the recorded deaths, which are large, and the vast number of unrecorded deaths that must take place amongst wild foxes, these have no apparent effect on the fox population level. The fox not only survives but thrives, despite man's determined efforts to destroy him.

Appendices

1965
November 1 Woodchester foxes active (near Stroud)
          14 'Woo-wo-woo' at Hownhall, 8.45 pm (3 miles from Kent's Green)
              From 10th to 17th much barking about 6 pm

December 19 Taynton, 'wo-wo-wo' and 'wo-wo'. Also high, short yapping and single yells 'wo' ↗ ; 5.50 to 9.30 pm, also at Kent's Green, 10.15 pm, 'wo-wo-wo'
          21 Taynton, 'wo-wo-wo', one with howl 6.10 to 6.20 pm
          25 Taynton, 5.45 pm 'wo-wo-wo' barking and yelling 6.20 to 6.25 pm 'wo-wo-wo' and hysterical screams. One light 'yap-yap-yap'
          26 5.40 pm, contact bark Savage's, 7.30 'wo ↗' yell
          27 5.5. pm, 'wo-wo-wo' Big Pit lasted until 9.40, then short spell of sharp yelling, 'wo' ↗ one 'wo-wo-wo' in middle
          28 Kent's Green, 9.40 pm 'wo-wo', some with yells at end 24 in 5 minutes. Savage's to Big Pit area
          29 Yelling and screaming from near Grange Earth lasted about 30 seconds, no other noise
          30 Barking 8.40 to 9.30 pm Big Pit area, short 'wo-wo's' only
          31 'Wo-wo's' around 8 pm

1966
January 1 7.45 pm, fox barking in Savage's field, also along Woodman's orchard 'wo-wo's'. 11 pm 'wo-wo-wo' along Woodman's valley
          2 Near Taynton Church, 4.50 pm
          3 From 7 pm, barking along Woodman's valley.

Barks and howls near stream 8 to 8.15 pm

4 6.30 pm, Kent's Green, 'wo-wo', 'wo-wo-owo' and 'wo ↗' in Woodman's orchard. No noise after 7.45 pm

4 9.10 pm, 'wow ↗' near Woodman's, single with long pauses

5 5.4 pm, Woodman's, 'wo-wo-wo'; 6.15–20 anxious bark Taynton Court, 'wo-wo-wo' and shriek, single 'wo ↗', much barking single double and triple, up to 9.50 pm

6 6 pm, 'wo-wo' howl at 6.15 Woodman's

7 6.30 pm, Woodman's until 10.45. Between Woodman's and Clewes' 9 to 9.45 pm. Three different foxes no howls

8 6 to 7.45 pm, three separate foxes all barking together, ceased 10 pm. Single yells
9.30 to 9.45 pm, 'wo-wo' and 'wo-wo-wo' and yell near Woodman's. Light yapping from Big Pit

9 6 pm, single bark, 7.15 pm, 'wo-wo' fox between Taynton Court and Hussey's; 9 pm, hysterical fox—Wintal's

11 7.30 pm, near Grove for 20 minutes, hysterical fox only

13 Near Taynton council houses, hysterical fox but subdued soft 'woow' and 'wo-wo-wo', no yells

14 Woodchester, soft yodel 'wowoo', 4.30 pm, daylight

15 Taynton barking, 5.40 pm

16 6 to 8.30 pm, near Clewes' farm, 'wo-wo' fox

17 6.5 to 6.25 pm, 'wo-wo-wo', then two and three notes until 10.50 pm

18 6.20 pm, Taynton Court farm from Clewes', 'wo-wo' fox; 9.20 in Woodman's orchard

21 5.30, at Clewes', near Pit, recorded three double barks; 8 pm, at Gabb's for five minutes

22 7 p.m., at Clewes', only three barks after this 'wo-wo's between Woodsman's and Gabbs'.

23 8.40 pm, near Woodman's

24 No barks

25 5.15 pm, one sharp bark then 'wo-wo-wo' hoarse high-pitched, Big Pit

	20 & 30	No barking
	31	8 pm, awful shrieking and yelling Savage's field lasted about 3 minutes
February	3	No barking last few days
	6	9.20 pm, towards Woodman's, rapid 'wo-wo-wo', also a number of screams
	8	'Wo-wo' and howls from Woodman's, also near Hussey's and Clewes'
		One prolonged spell of shouting like a duck being slowly strangled, noise from 8.20 to 9.30 pm
	19	7.25 pm, 'wo ↗' yells from Woodman's
March	9	Screaming reported from Lasborough, cubs also heard underground. (Cotswolds near Tetbury.)
	12	Woodchester, yells only 'wo→'
	19	'oo ↗'s' in Hook's farm direction
May	2	Cub barking at Small Pond Earth 'ŏw-ŏw-ŏw'
	9	Cub barking at Grange Earth
	15	Single bark, 9 pm, Clewes'
	18	Many single yells 'wo ↗' at midnight
June	1	Much single yelling, 1.30 to 2 am, around Kent's Green Farm
	2	Barking at 11 pm near Savage's, five single yells
	5	Fox? going to cubs barked at me, single yells 10.5 pm 'wo ↗'
	9	Single yell, 10 pm
	16	Cubs heard near Three Oaks, 10.10 pm
	31	Much cub yapping in hedge
July	15	Single shrieks in Woodman's orchard after 10 pm
August	15	11 pm, two single yells 'oo ↗-oo ↗'
	19	Fighting cubs heard 9.10 pm Savage's hedge
	21	Fighting cubs heard 9.15 pm
	23	Fighting cubs heard 9.15 pm
	24	Fighting cubs heard 8.30 pm
September	15	Single yells, 41 counted, moving fox Kent's Green ↗
October	28	11 pm, 'qw̆qwqwqwooh' repeated with few seconds' pause, also fighting and yelling

5 am terrific fighting noise from orchard ? cubs 'fighting' or adults courting

29 'Fighting' again, soft 'qwqwqw' type at about midnight

2 am, single howling Woodman's

November 6 8 pm, single yells in Clewes' fields again heard at about 11 pm, near Hussey's

7 8 pm, cubs briefly in Woodman's orchard, then single yells and 'cluck-cluck-cluck' call. One or two longer yells

Fighting in the distance below Clewes' Farm

8 Short, urgent barking, no whine at end, 8 to 9 pm

9 Barking at 8.45 pm, short single few calls heard, brief shrieks

Note. The small arrows in some of the calls indicate a rise or fall in the pitch of the note.

B Scent and scenting conditions

Animals like ourselves can only smell substances when they are in a gaseous state and the gases are dissolved in the fluid covering the soft membranes of the nose. It is for this reason that a healthy animal's nose is moist.

The smell receptors occur in small, blind pockets from which the main current of air is excluded. Air containing 'smellable' particles is carried into the pockets, either by diffusion or by convection currents. These latter are set up when cold-inspired air meets the warmer air in the nostrils, as by a quick, short inspiration or sniff. Sniffing is, therefore, a necessary operation in creating the correct internal conditions for detecting a smell.

Human beings soon get used to a particular smell and become insensitive to it for a time. Does this apply to foxes also and, if so, how do they remain on a scent for a long period? How, likewise, does a hound follow a fox? May not the fact that dogs and foxes run with their mouths open be something to do with this? Whilst air is being breathed by mouth, no smell is being detected, but when they stop to check the line the mouth is closed and the characteristic sniffing goes on till they rediscover the line—which may involve considerable casting about.

When we become used to a particular smell, we can no longer detect it but we can still smell other substances. Something like this must surely apply to the fox, for its own smell would otherwise be always with it and dominate others more subtle. In other words, the fox must be used to its own smell and be unconscious of it.

It is possible to mix two highly-smelling substances together in certain proportions so that they have no effect on the organs of scent. For example, 4 grm of iodoform in 200 grm of Peruvian balsam is said to be almost odourless, even if the two substances are placed in separate tubes and inserted one in each nostril. I wonder if the secretion from the dorsal tail gland which is said to have an 'ambrosial' odour, can in this way counter the anal gland secretion?

174

Linnaeus, no less, thought that this was the function of the caudal gland.

I have said that a fox has an extremely well-developed sense of smell which it uses both in locating food and in avoiding enemies. The foot glands of the fox leave a scent upon the ground over which it moves and this marking of the trail may be of use to the animal when it retraces its steps. As the fox normally moves in a very well-known region, I do not think the foot scent is of importance to the animal that makes it but it does give information to other foxes in the area. The most important function of this scent may be in keeping the animals apart. It can and does, however, work against the fox, as its trail can be followed by other animals of another species. Hounds seem to hunt mainly the foot scent of the fox, as wolves probably did when they lived in this country.

Neither the foot gland nor the anal gland secretions seem to be under the conscious control of the fox. The foot scent is liberated involuntarily whenever the fox moves.

Anal glands are well-developed in the *Mustelidae* family, which includes the badger, stoat, weasel, polecat, pine marten and otter in this country, and the notorious skunk in North America. In the case of the skunk the scent provides an excellent defence, although in the majority of *Mustelids* its main function is probably to provide a means of marking the animal's territory, in which case there is probably some voluntary control of the secretion. In the badger, Neal believes that the characteristic musky smell is produced when the animal is surprised or excited. I believe this is also the case with the fox. When first disturbed by a hunting animal it reacts by producing, quite involuntarily, a discharge of anal gland scent; this gradually wears off and the fox is then followed along its foot trail. If another fox is put up during the hunt, this would react by producing more anal gland scent, which might account for the change in voice of the hounds as they follow a fresh line.

The intensity of the foot trail scent will presumably be partly dependent on the surface over which the animal travels. The scent itself is a fluid which adheres to the substratum and the ability of different types of substratum to pick up scent may be due to the state of division of that surface. A surface made up of small particles, such as a good loamy soil, presents a large surface area for the foot gland secretion to cover and also provides water in which the scent can be dissolved. Dry smooth surfaces, such as roadways and railway lines,

M   175

are unlikely to be able to hold scent for very long. The scent will tend to evaporate quickly from a smooth surface but cling to and be slowly released by soil. Soil will be said, therefore, to hold scent much better than tarmacadam. The amount of a substance that can be taken into solution depends partly upon the state of division of the substratum.

Once the trail has been laid, the rate at which the scent is given off into the atmosphere as a gas will depend partly upon atmospheric temperature and pressure. A warm dry day with some wind will result in a fairly rapid release and dissipation of the scent. The latter, when we smell it, is a collection of fairly heavy molecules produced by the evaporation of the scent fluid that is deposited by the fox. These relatively heavy molecules will tend to hang in a heavy atmosphere, and the height to which they rise will depend upon the atmospheric pressure.

If a layer of cold air covers a warm layer of air next to the ground, a common night condition, then the heavy cold air will prevent the scent particles from rising, so giving good scenting conditions for a hunting animal. When the ground is warm, as when the sun is shining, the scent should rise and be of little use to a ground hunting animal, although possibly still detectable by a human nose, particularly if its owner is horse-mounted.

A day of fairly high barometric pressure should provide better conditions for fox foot scent to be absorbed by soil particles, so producing a fairly long-lasting trail which hounds can follow. Conversely, a low pressure day should not provide such good conditions for scent retention and, judging by hunting literature, this seems to be the case.

I have spoken so far about scent on soil particles, but it will also cling to grass and other vegetation. In this case also the scent is most probably in solution, which presupposes that the vegetation is wet or at least damp. The scent on vegetation is also in temporary solution and will be released under similar conditions as soil scent. Much water will tend greatly to dilute the scent and so reduce the possibility of following the trail. In frosts, there is no liquid in which to dissolve the scent, and such as is present will tend to hang in the air.

I believe there is nothing mystical about fox scent, as is often suggested; it is only necessary to apply the chemical knowledge we have about the behaviour of liquids and gases under different conditions of temperature and pressure. If we do this, we can predict that scenting conditions should be good (a) at night or any time when a cold layer of air lies very close to a warm thin layer of air over the ground; (b) on warm moist days with indirect sun. In both cases there should be little wind.

C   The weights of foxes in kilograms

Country	Average weight			Maximum weight recorded
	Male		Female	
Norway	5·9	5·55	5·2	14·3
Denmark				12·0
Finland		5·01		8·05
Swedan				11·1
Germany				13·0
Scotland	7·4		6·2	8·62
England	6·7		5·4	10·4
USSR				11·4
USA	5·3		4·2	6·09

Based mainly on information given by Lund, but also from Ognev and Mathews (1951)

D Table of comparative cranial measurements (in centimetres)

Measurement	Scottish		English		Scandinavian (V.v. vulpes)		Russian	
	Range	Average	Range	Average	Range	Average	Range	Average
Condylobasal l.	138·5–157·0	150·7	135·0–151·5	144·6	135·4–155·0	147·1	140·5–151·3	149·4
Zygomatic w.	81·0–85·5	83·2	76·0–86·0	81·9	73·0–83·0	78·8	73·2–87·0	79·9
Inter-orbital w.	27·5–33·0	29·6	25·0–32·5	30·3	23·0–30·6	28·2	27·0–33·6	29·9
Mandible l.	113·0–124·5	118·8	103·5–117·5	112·5	103·0–121·6	113·4		
Maxillary tooth row	66·5–72·5	69·3	61·0–69·0	64·9	61·1–74·0	68·4		
Mandibular tooth row	72·5–82·0	78·5	69·0–77·0	73·1	69·6–84·8	77·0	62·3–69·9	66·8
Upper carnasial l.	15·0–17·0	16·2	14·0–15·5	14·8	14·2–17·0	15·9	72·0–77·9	74·9
Upper carnasial w.	8·0–9·0	8·3	6·5–8·5	7·2	7·6–8·8	7·9		
Lower carnasial l.	16·0–17·0	16·3	14·5–16·5	15·7	14·2–17·8	16·3		
Lower carnasial w.	6·0–7·0	6·6	6·0–6·5	6·3	6·0–6·4	6·1		

Information from Miller, Ognev, Hattingh and Tetley

E   Graph showing monthly fluctuations in fox weight

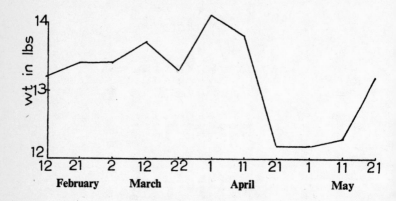

Information from Hattingh (1956): weights of dog fox and vixen combined

F Fox body-length measurements

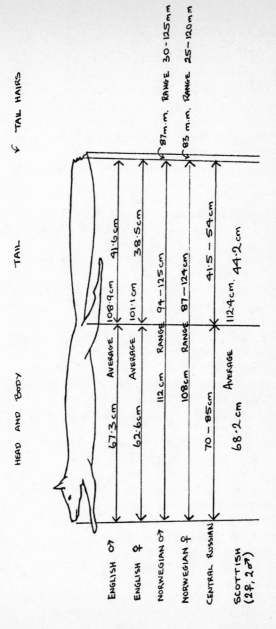

HEAD AND BODY   TAIL   & TAIL HAIRS

ENGLISH ♂   67·3 cm AVERAGE 108·9 cm   41·6 cm

ENGLISH ♀   62·6 cm AVERAGE 101·1 cm   38·5 cm

NORWEGIAN ♂   112 cm RANGE 94 – 125 cm

NORWEGIAN ♀   108 cm RANGE 87 – 124 cm   87 m.m. RANGE 30 – 125 mm

CENTRAL RUSSIAN   70 – 85 cm   41·5 – 54 cm   83 m.m. RANGE 25 – 120 mm

SCOTTISH
(2♀, 2♂)   68·2 cm AVERAGE 112·4 cm. 44·2 cm

Bibliography

Ashbrook, F. G. (1937). 'The breeding of fur animals', *Yearbook of Agriculture*, 1937, 1379–95.

Avaliani, R., 'Ecology of the Transcaucasian steppe fox *Vulpes vulpes alpherakyi* in the Gruzinian SSR', From ref *ZH. Biol* 1964, No. 161274 (Translation).

Baranovskaya, T. N. & Kolosov, A. M. (1935). *Die Nahrung des Fuchses (Vulpes vulpes L.)*. In Russian; summary in German, Zool. Zh., 14, 3, 523–50. Moskwa.

Bassett, C. F. & Llewellyn (1947). 'Canadian Silver Fox and Fur', Sept & Oct 1947.

Bernard, J. (1959). *'Note sur le periode de reproduction du renard Vulpes vulpes L. dans le Luxembourge belge,'* Saugetierk Mitt. 7, 110–13.

Blackmore, D. K. (1964). 'Survey of diseases in British wild foxes (*Vulpes vulpes*)'. *Vet Rec* 76: 527–55.

Blackmore, D. K. (1963). 'The toxicity of some chlorinated hydro-carbons insecticides to British wild foxes', *J Comp Pathol Therap* 73 (4), 391–409.

Butler, L. (1945). 'Colour phases of the red fox in Canada', *Genetics*, 30, 39–50.

Churcher, C. S. (1959). 'The specific status of the New World red foxes', *J Mammal* 40, 513–20.

Cook, D. B. & Hamilton, W. S. (1944). 'The ecological relationships of red fox food in Eastern New York', *Ecology* 25, 91–104.

Corbet, G. B. (1963). 'The frequency of albinism of the tail tip in British Mammals', *Proc Zoo Soc* Lond 140, 327–30.

Corbet, G. B. (1964). 'The identification of British Mammals', Brit Mus (Nat Hist).

Creed, R. F. S. (1960). 'Gonad changes in the wild red fox *Vulpes vulpes crucigera*', *J Physiol* 151, 19–20.

Creed, R. F. S. (1960). 'Observations on reproduction in the wild red fox (*Vulpes vulpes*)', *Brit Vet J* 116, 419–26.

Day, M. G. (1966). 'Identification of hairs and feather remains in the gut and faeces of stoats and weasels', *J Zool* 148, 201–17.

Dearborn, N. (1939). 'Sections aid in identifying hair', *J Mammal* 20, 346–8.

Douglas, M. J. W. (1956). 'Notes on the red fox (*Vulpes vulpes*) near Braemar Scotland', *J Zool* 147, 228–33.

Elton, C. (1927). *Animal Ecology*, Oxford.

Ellerman, J. H. & Morrison-Scott, T. C. S. (1951). 'Checklist of Palaearctic and Indian Mammals', Brit Mus (Nat Hist) London.

Errington, P. L. (1935). 'Food habits of mid-west foxes', *J Mammal* 16, 192–200.

Errington, P. L. (1937). 'Food habits of Iowa red foxes during a drought', *Ecology* 18, 53–61.

Errington, P. L. & Berry, R. M. (1937). 'Tagging studies of red foxes', *J Mammal* 18, 203–5.

Fitzgerald, B. Vesey- (1965). *Town Fox, Country Fox*, Deutsch.

Gilmore, R. M. (1946). 'Mammals in archaeological collections from S.W. Pennsylvania', *J Mammal* 27, 227–35.

Gilmore, R. M. (1949). 'The identification and value of mammal bones from archaeological excavations', *J Mammal* 30, 163–9.

Hamilton, W. I. (1935). 'Notes on food of red foxes in New York and New England', *J Mammal* 16, 16–21.

Hatfield, D. M. (1939). 'Winter food habits of foxes in Minnesota', *J Mammal* 20, 202–6.

Hattingh, I. (1956). 'Measurements of foxes from Scotland and England', *Proc Zool Soc* Lond 138, 137–55.

Hediger, H. (1955). *Studies of the Psychology and Behaviour of animals in Zoos and Circuses*, Butterworth.

Hoffman, R. A. & Kirkpatrick, C. M. (1954). 'Red fox weights and reproduction in Tippecanoe County, Indiana', *J Mammal* 35, 504–9.

Hurrell, H. G. (1962). 'Foxes', Sunday Times Publ Animals of Britain, No 9.

Iljina, E. D. (1934). 'The inheritance of the colour in foxes', Zool Zurn 13, 701–13.

Karpuleon, F. (1958). 'Food habits of Wisconsin Foxes', *J Mammal* 39, 591–3.

Kleinman, D. (1966) in Jewell, P. A. & Loizos, C. Ed. *Play, Exploration and Territory in Mammals*, Academic Press.

Korschgen, L. J. (1959). 'Food habits of the red fox in Missouri', *J Wildlife Manag* 23, 168–76.

Kruuk, H. (1965). *Predatory and anti-predatory behaviour of the black-headed gull*, Leiden, E. J. Brill.

Lampio, T. (1953). 'On the food of the fox', *Suomen Riista* 8, 156–64.

Lande, O. (1958). 'Chromosome number in the silver fox', *Nature*, London 181, 1353–4.

Leutcher, A. (1960). *Tracks and Signs of British Animals*, Cleaver-Hume Press, London.

Lever, R. A. (1957). 'Two records of foxes eating larval hoverflies and dor beetles', *Proc Zool Soc* Lond 128, 596–7.

Lever, R. A. (1959). 'Diet of the fox since myxomatosis', *J Anim Ecol* 28, 359–75.

Lever, R. A., Armour, C. J., Thompson, H. V. (1957). 'Myxomatosis and the fox', *Agriculture* 64, 105–11.

Lockie, J. D. (1956). 'After myxomatosis', *Scot Agric* 36, 65–9.

Lockie, J. D. (1959). 'Estimation of the food of foxes', *Wildlife Mgmt* 23, 224–7.

Lockie, J. D. (1961). 'The food of the pine marten, *Martes martes*, in West Ross-shire, Scotland', *Proc Zool Soc* Lond 136, 187–95.

Lorenz, K. *Man meets dog*, Methuen (1954).

Lorenz, K. *On Aggression*, Methuen (1966).

Lord, R. D. (1961). 'A population study of the gray fox', *Amer Midl Nat* 66, 87–109

Lund, M-K. (1959). 'The red fox in Norway', Pap Norweg Game-Res 5, No 2.

Mathews, L. H. (1951). 'A large Scottish fox', *Proc Zoo Soc* Lond 120, 4, 679–81.

Mathews, L. H. (1952). *British Mammals*, Collins.

McIntosh, D. L. 'Reproduction and growth of the fox in the Canberra district', *CRISO Wildlife Res* 8 (2), 131–41.

Merriam, H. G. (1963). 'An unusual fox–woodchuck relationship', *J Mammal* 44.

Middleton, A. D. (1957). 'Game birds on the farm' (2), *Agriculture* 64, 345–7.

Millais, J. G. (1904–6). *Mammals of Great Britain and Ireland*, Longmans Green, 3 vols, London.

Miller, G. S. (1912). *Catalogue of the mammals of Western Europe*, Brit Mus (Nat Hist) London.

Mivart, St. G. (1890). *A Monograph of the Canidae*, R. H. Porter, London.

Murie, A. (1936). 'Following fox trails', Mis publ Mus Zool Univ of Michigan, No 32. 1–45.

Murie, O. J. (1946). 'Evaluating duplications in analysis of coyote scats', *J Wildlife Mgmt* 10, 275–7.

Neal, E. G. (1948). *The Badger*, Collins.

Nelson, A. L. (1933). 'The food of Virginian foxes', *J Mammal* 14, 40–3.

Novikov, G. A. (1956). 'Carnivorous Mammals of the fauna of the USSR', Moscow & Leningrad, Keys to the fauna of the USSR, No 62. Translation 1962 by Israel Program for Sci Trans.

Ognev, S. I. (1931). 'Mammals of Eastern Europe and N. Asia II Carnivora'. Translation 1962 by Israel Program for Sci Trans.

Oksala, T. (1954). 'Genetics of the dark phases of the red fox in experiment and nature', Pap Game Res Helsinki, No 11, 3–16.

Oksala, T. (1954). 'On the Samson character of the red fox', Pap Game Res Helsinki, No 11, 17–23.

Peterson, R. L., Standfield, R. O., McEwen, E. H. & Brooks, A. C. (1953). 'Early records of the red and grey fox in Ontario', *J Mammal* 34, 126–7.

Pocock, R. I. (1941). *The fauna of British India (Carnivora)*, Taylor & Francis.

Rowlands, I. W. & Parkes, A. S. (1935). 'The reproductive processes of various mammals. VIII: Reproduction in Foxes' (*Vulpes* spp), *Proc Zool Soc* Lond 105, 823–41.

Sande, J. O. (1943). 'Hvordan reven hamstrer om vinteren', *Naturen*, 255–6.

Seton, E. T. (1910). *Life Histories of Northern animals, Vol II*, Constable.

Seton, E. T. (1929). *Lives of game animals*, New York.

Schofield, R. D. (1960). 'A thousand miles of fox trails in Michigan's ruffed grouse range', *J Wildlife Mgmt* 24, 432–4.

Scott, T. G. (1941). 'A method of estimating the red fox population', Iowa State Coll, *J Sci* 15, 155–9.

Scott, T. G. (1943). 'Methods and computation in fecal analysis with reference to the red fox', Iowa State Coll, *J Sci* 15, 279–85.

Scott, T. G. (1943). 'Some food coactions of the Northern Plains red fox, *Ecol Monog* 13, 427–79.

Scott, T. G. & Klimstra, W. D. (1955). 'Red foxes and a declining prey population', Monog Univ S Ill, No 1.

Shawinski, et al (1962). 'Rocz Nauk Roliczych', Ser B 80 (2), 187–98.

Sheldon, W. G. (1950) & (1953). 'Returns on banded red and gray foxes in New York State', *J Wildlife Mgmt* 14, 33–44 & *J Mammal* 34, 125.

Sheldon, W. G. (1949). 'Reproductive behaviour of foxes in New York State', *J Mammal* 30, 236–46.

Smith, L. F. (1943). 'Internal parasites of the red fox in Iowa', *J Wildlife Mgmt* 7, 174–8.

Southern, H. N. & Watson, J. S. (1941). 'Summer food of the red fox in Great Britain', *J Anim Ecol* 10, 1–11.

Southern, H. N. Ed. (1964). *Handbook of British Mammals*, Blackwell.

Switzenberg, D. F. (1950). 'Breeding productivity in Michigan red foxes', *J Mammal* 31, 194–5.

Talbot, J. S. (1906). 'Foxes at home', Horace Cox, *The Field*.

Tembrock, G. (1957). 'Zur Ethologie des Rotfuchses (*Vulpes vulpes* (*L*)), unter besondere Berucksichtigung der Fortpflanzung', Zool Gart Lpzg 23, 289–532.

Tembrock, G. (1958). 'Spielverhalten beim Rotfuchs', Zool Britr Berl 3, 423–96.

Tembrock, G. (1958). 'Zur Aktivitatsperiodik bei Vulpes und Alopex Zool, Jb (Allg Zool) 68, 297–324.

Tembrock G. (1960). 'Zeitsch Tierpsychol', 16 (3), 351–68.

Tetley, H. (1941). 'On the Scottish Fox', *Proc Zool Soc* Lond 111B, 23–35.

Usinger, A. (1934). 'Question of monogamous or polygamous relations between male and female in the silver and red fox', Der Deutsche Palzatierzuechter, Munich Jahrg 9, 23.

Vincent, R. E. (1958). 'Observations on red fox behaviour', *Ecology* 39, 755–7.

Voipio, L. (1950). 'Evolution of population levels', Papers on Game research, 5, 1–176.

Watson, A. (1955). 'The winter food of six Highland foxes', Scot Nat 67, 123–4.

Wildman, A. B. (1954). 'The microscopy of animal textile fibres', Leeds Wool Industries Research Association.

Wood, J. E. (1959). 'Relative estimates of fox population levels', *J Wildlife Manag* 23, 53–63.

Index